The Borzoletti Monstrance

A mystery

Norman Robbins

Samuel French — London
www.samuelfrench-london.co.uk

Please see page iv for further copyright information

CHARACTERS

David Reeves-Mercer, late 20s
Jean Reeves-Mercer, 25
Harold Crossley, about 30
Brenda Treshunt, late 70s
Austin Reeves-Mercer, early 50s
Father Carmody, late 60s
Marcia Vale, 70s
Iona Vale, 40s
Sylvia Jones, 40s

SYNOPSIS OF SCENES

The action of the play takes place in the Terrace Room of Redston Hall, Kent, home of the Reeves-Mercer family since 1769

ACT I
SCENE 1 An August morning
SCENE 2 The same day, early afternoon

ACT II
SCENE 1 Ten days later, mid-afternoon
SCENE 2 Late morning, the following day

Time — the present

COPYRIGHT INFORMATION

For my son and daughter-in-law

Adam and Anne

Other plays and pantomimes
by Norman Robbins
published by Samuel French Ltd

And Evermore Shall Be So
At The Sign of "The Crippled Harlequin"
Aladdin
Ali Baba and the Forty Thieves
Babes in the Wood
Cinderella
Dick Whittington
The Dragon of Wantley
The Grand Old Duke of York
Hansel and Gretel
Hickory Dickory Dock
Humpty Dumpty
Jack and Jill
Jack and the Beanstalk
The Late Mrs Early
Nightmare
The Old Woman Who Lived in a Shoe
Practice to Deceive
Prepare to Meet Thy Tomb
Prescription for Murder
Pull the Other One
Puss in Boots
Red Riding Hood
Rumpelstiltzkin
Sing a Song of Sixpence
Slaughterhouse
Sleeping Beauty
Snow White
Tiptoe Through the Tombstones
Tom, the Piper's Son
A Tomb with a View
Wedding of the Year
The White Cat
The Wonderful Story of Mother Goose

ACT I

Scene 1

The Terrace Room of Redston Hall. An August morning

The room is quite imposing. Almost all the rear wall is occupied by a series of french windows, that lead out on to a broad, balustraded terrace overlooking a mature garden and distant hills. To the R of the terrace, a small table and two chairs are set, and L, a lounger and parasol. On the table, the remains of a breakfast can be seen. On the parapet, a half-empty glass of orange juice stands, opposite an open window. Heavy-looking pelmets and curtains hang at the windows. L of the window is a door leading into the room beyond. Upstage of the L wall is a long table, and on this stand a marble bust, a table lamp, a bowl of flowers, and a framed photograph of a dog. Over this, a pair of wall-mounted lamps. Downstage of the table are double doors that lead out to a hall, the kitchen, upstairs, etc., and these doors are open. Left of them are light switches that control both the central light and the wall-mounted lights. Further downstage, a writing desk and chair with matching wall lamps above, and downstage of these, another small table on which stands a bronze statuette and a bowl of ceramic flowers. The wall R is dominated by a central white marble fireplace and surround. Wall lamps are at each side of this. Fire-dogs, irons, etc. are in the hearth, contained by a white fender. Below the fireplace is a door leading into the library, and upstage of the fireplace, a door leading into the music room. Slightly upstage of the fireplace, a comfortable-looking easy chair is angled towards it, and a large matching sofa is L, also slightly angled R. Behind this, a long, narrow table on which a vase of flowers stands. In front of the sofa, a long, low, coffee table. A mixture of portraits, scenic views, tapestries and framed photographs fill almost every other inch of wall space, and the room is thickly carpeted. The whole effect should be money, comfort, age and upper class

When the scene begins, sunlight bathes the terrace. David Reeves-Mercer is on his back atop the sofa, feet resting on the arm R, apparently fast asleep. He is in his late twenties, though looks younger, and is usually totally care-free in attitude. He wears only a light, unfastened dressing gown, bedroom slippers and garish boxer shorts. Discarded newspaper

*sections litter the coffee table and the space around it, and a single
section rests on his stomach, under his downstage arm*

*After a moment, a bleary-eyed Jean Reeves-Mercer enters through the
double doors, wearing a pale silk pyjama suit, and slippers, topped
with a silky dressing gown. She is slightly younger and more volatile
than her brother, and at the moment, appears to be suffering from a bad
hangover. She is sipping at the mug of coffee she carries as she enters*

Jean (*seeing David and groaning*) Oh, God. A naked poof on the sofa.
That's all I need before breakfast. (*She halts at the L end of the sofa
and behind it*)

David (*without moving*) Morning.

Jean (*sourly*) What are you doing here? Boyfriend kicked you out, has
he?

David (*raising his head*) Quite the reverse, dear heart. I've brought him
down for the weekend.

Jean (*dismayed*) You haven't.

David If we're going to have a civil partnership, I had to let him meet
his future in-laws.

Jean (*glancing round distastefully*) Where is he?

David (*wickedly*) Now you've tottered out of it, probably in your room,
trying on your frocks.

Jean (*hotly*) If he lays a finger ——

David (*sitting up; exasperated*) Oh, knock it off, Jean. How many times
have I told you? He's not gay, and neither am I. We share an apartment.
For *financial* reasons. And the only reason he won't want to bed you
on sight is because he happens to have excellent taste. (*Pointedly*)
Which is more than I can say for the (*scornfully*) honourable George
de Vere Milland.

Jean Gorgeous George? (*Moving sluggishly to the easy chair*) What's
he got to do with it?

David (*smugly*) Obviously you've not seen the papers. According to the
Telegraph, he's just announced his engagement to the Telford trollop.

Jean (*in disbelief*) You're joking.

David (*tossing the paper over his head, towards her*) See for yourself.
(*He swings himself into a sitting position*) Face like a bottle of warts
and ten stone overweight, but Daddy left her sixty million, so she
attracts men like a compost heap draws flies. (*In mock sympathy*) Lost
out again, dear heart. Sex doesn't stand a chance against the chinky
chink chink of gold.

Jean (*sitting, and ignoring the paper*) Get stuffed. (*Defensively*) He's
not at all like that. If he's going to marry Sophie Telford, it must be

because he loves her. He wouldn't propose just because her father left her a fortune. (*She sips at the coffee*)

David (*standing*) True, I suppose. He'd have done it *whoever* had left it to her.

Jean (*scowling*) Oh, cover yourself up. You look like an ad for a porno mag ... If Treasure walked in, you'd give her a heart attack.

David (*moving round to the windows*) Very unlikely, dear. She's seen it all before. She was changing my nappies and powdering my bum before you were even born. (*Thoughtfully*) Mind you ... I think she's got the hots for me now. She dished up breakfast an hour ago in a pink thong and no bra. (*He steps on to the terrace and raises his arms to the sun*) Definitely not her colour.

Jean (*ignoring this*) Where's Dad?

David (*turning*) In the study. With Father C.

Jean (*groaning*) Oh, God. What's *he* want?

David (*supporting himself on the frame*) Another shot at converting us, I expect. How should *I* know? You're the fixture. I'm just the visiting black sheep. (*He bleats*)

Jean (*sourly*) And how long do we have to endure you this time? (*She sips at the coffee*)

David (*shrugging*) All depends. If he coughs up the necessary, we could be gone Sunday night. (*Lightly*) On the other hand ...

Jean You'll dig your grubby little claws in, till you've worn him down.

David (*grinning*) Such an elegant turn of phrase. But not short of the mark. What's the point of being a Reeves-Mercer if you can't spend your ancestors' ill-gotten gains?

Jean (*dryly*) It may have escaped your notice, David, but we're not exactly rolling in it, these days. We still owe thousands in death duties.

David (*lightly*) Which shouldn't be a problem for much longer.

Jean (*frowning*) Why's that?

David (*disgustedly*) Don't you read anything but *OK* and *Harper's Bazaar*? Work it out for yourself? I'm going to join Harold. (*He turns back on to the terrace*)

Jean In the garden?

David In the pool. If you peep over here, you can see him in all his glory. (*He peers over the parapet. Calling*) Oy. There's a lady present. Get your trunks on, you filthy swine.

Jean (*annoyed*) He's not naked?

David (*turning his head to her*) As the day he was born. (*Calling down again*) I never knew you were *Jewish*, Harry. (*He laughs*) Who was your dad? A bloody elephant?

Jean (*standing*) Get him out of there, now.

Harold Crossley enters through the double doors L. *He is about 30,
dressed in light slacks, a short-sleeved shirt and casual shoes*

Jean sees him

(*Sharply*) Who are *you*? (*She clutches her dressing gown to her*)
Harold (*taken aback*) Harold Crossley. David's flatmate. (*Quizzically*)
Jean??

David moves back to the windows, looking amused

Jean (*tightly*) He said you were in the pool. Without your trunks.

Harold looks blank and shakes his head

(*To David; glowering*) Was that supposed to be funny?
David (*stepping into the room*) It made *me* laugh ... And it serves you
right for jumping to conclusions. (*To Harold*) My sweet little sister
thought we were gay.

Jean looks furious and embarrassed

Harold (*frowning*) What?
David (*moving down between them*) Because of the flat share.
Harold Oh. (*Smiling at Jean*) Well you needn't worry on that account.
We're strictly *hetero*sexual. (*To David*) Aren't we, Dave? (*He puts
his arm around David's shoulder and gives him a hearty kiss on the
cheek*)
David (*yelping in fright*) Get off. (*He frantically pushes him away*)
Harold (*reproachfully*) You didn't say that last night.
David (*annoyed*) Knock it off, bird-brain. (*Hastily wrapping his
dressing gown round him and fastens the belt*) She'll think we *are*
gay, now.
Harold (*raising an eyebrow*) With a reputation like yours? (*To Jean*)
Believe me. He makes Casanova look like an amateur. It's a good job
you're living down here, and not in London. What you don't see, you
don't have to worry about.
Jean (*dryly*) The day *he* worries me's the day I'll ride on horseback
down High Street, stark naked. (*She sits again*)
David (*to Harold*) See? I told you she was weird. Better get you out of
here before you go blind in one eye.
Harold (*frowning*) What?
David (*explaining*) It happened to *him*, you know. Peeping Tom. When
he looked at her.

Harold (*blankly*) Who?

David (*sighing deeply*) Lady Godiva, you berk.

Jean (*to Harold, wearily*) Just ignore him, Harold. I'm sure you must do normally.

David (*indignantly*) No, he doesn't. He breathes in every word I utter. (*Smugly*) He may be only a commoner ...

Harold reacts

... but he appreciates having a superior being for a flatmate ... if only for the benefit of my classical education. (*Grandly*) And now ... if you'll excuse me ... I'll withdraw to my room and change to more suitable attire. (*To Harold, in normal tones*) They're a bit conservative in these parts, so if I'm going to show you round town, I'd better wear something decent. (*He heads for the double doors*)

Jean (*sharply*) And not my Jasper Conran. I've only worn it twice.

David glowers at her then exits

Harold (*after a moment*) He's not gay, you know.

Jean No. But he *is* a pain in the backside, and it winds him up when he thinks I think he is. How you can share a flat with him, I can't imagine.

Harold (*moving to the sofa and sitting*) We don't see each other much, to be honest. I'm usually at work before he surfaces, and he's on the town by the time I get back. It's only weekends we get in each other's way. (*Sighing*) Still ... one more rent rise, and I'll have to be looking for somewhere cheaper. The outgoings are almost more than the income. God knows how some people manage.

Jean (*with feeling*) Tell me about it. Just because we've lived here since Dick's days, the locals think we're rolling in it. Little do they know.

Harold I suppose it'll help if the sale goes through. The Americans'll jump at it, of course. Or the Russians. *They're* not short of a rouble or two.

Jean (*frowning*) We're not selling the place. Did he say we were?

Harold (*hastily*) No, no. I didn't mean the Hall. I meant the Monstrance.

Jean (*blankly*) Monstrance?

Harold From the Convent.

Jean (*baffled*) Do you mind if we start again? I haven't a clue what you're on about.

Harold Well ... they're closing it down, aren't they? Moving the nuns to a rest home, or something? I heard about it on the grapevine.

Jean (*staring at him*) St Gudrun's, you mean?

Harold (*uncertainly*) I suppose so.

Jean (*amused*) Of course they're not closing it down. It's been there for centuries. Three of them, at least. One of our relatives was a nun there.

Harold (*nodding*) David told me. An ancestor's sister, wasn't it? The one who persuaded Sir Martin to donate the Monstrance to them?

Jean (*dismissively*) So the story goes. Though we don't know if it's true or not.

Harold (*frowning*) But ——

Jean It's possible. Of course it is. The old boy was richer than Midas. And he did take Lady C to Florence for their honeymoon. It's mentioned in his diaries. But there isn't a word about the Monstrance in them, and you'd think if he'd paid a fortune to have it made, he'd at least have mentioned it. I mean ... you don't donate a thing like that to the average convent, do you? And that's all the place was. Almost no one had ever heard of it. That's how it escaped the Reformation. What on earth would nuns want with a lump of gold encrusted with more jewels than Victoria's crown? They were an Order of Poverty, for God's sake.

Harold (*after a pause*) It's certainly a striking piece, though.

Jean (*pulling a face*) Too grotesque for my liking. (*She sips at her coffee*) Ugh. Cold.

Harold But typical Borzoletti, wouldn't you say? And maybe the finest piece he ever crafted. As I said ... the right collectors will give their eye teeth for it.

Jean I don't know which grapevine you've listened to, but if St Gudrun's *was* closing down, we'd have been the first to know about it. The family have been benefactors since seventeen sixty-nine ... though none of us are Catholics. (*She rises and moves towards the double doors* L) And if the rumour *was* true, there'd be no question of the Monstrance being put up for sale. It'd be given to a needy parish, or the missions in Africa. Religious items are never offered to the general public.

Harold (*awkwardly*) Not strictly true. Ecclesiastical items do turn up in sale-rooms round the country.

Jean (*halting by the door and turning to him*) Maybe paintings and things.

Harold And plate.

Jean (*firmly*) But not *consecrated* plate.

Harold I'm afraid so. Though it does lose its blessing the minute it's sold, I understand. I checked it out.

Jean (*moving back towards him*) But that's disgusting.

Harold (*shrugging*) Not really. It's more a case of making the best of your assets. I mean ... ornate things like a Monstrance hardly ever get *used* these days. Clergy are terrified at the thought of them being *stolen*, and insurance premiums are out of this world. Could you imagine the panic if the Borzoletti went missing? It must be worth millions.

Jean *(dryly)* A little optimistic, wouldn't you think? It's only an ornamental bread basket. A bit of gold and a handful of jewels.

Harold But made by Borzoletti. And that's the difference. It's the only known Monstrance he ever made, the only piece that's ended up in the UK, and the last thing he created before someone murdered him in seventeen seventy-three.

Jean *(frowning)* Who told you that? That he was murdered?

Harold It's in the new book about him. I was looking through it when I heard the news about the Convent closing and the Monstrance being put up for sale. Talk about coincidence.

Jean *(curious)* So why the interest in Borzoletti?

Harold The job, I suppose.

Jean looks at him blankly

Didn't Dave tell you? I work for Steadman and Waterfield. The Hatton Garden Goldsmiths.

Jean Oh. No. He didn't mention it. *(Curious)* So what else does it say about him?

Harold Not much more than we knew already. Though some of the colour plates are pretty amazing. The goblet he made for Pius the Sixth, for example ... and the Menari bowl that vanished when the Nazis took over in France. They're still in the dark about his parentage, though they've turned up a letter from the chap who adopted him in seventeen forty-five that suggests his mother may have been a foreigner of some kind. The only other new thing is a possibility his killer was some kind of nobleman. Possibly the husband of one of his conquests. *(He grins)* Something of a ladies' man, our Teodoro. At least eight are claiming direct descent, even though it puts them on the wrong side of the blanket, so to speak.

Brenda Treshunt enters through the double doors. She is a plump motherly woman in her late 70s, and Housekeeper to the family, though never treated as a servant by any of them. She carries an empty tray and crosses to the windows, intending to exit on to the terrace

He never married, you see?

Brenda *(as she walks)* If you're wanting breakfast, you'd better get a move on. They'll be clearing the room in ten minutes.

She goes on to the terrace and begins clearing the table R, stacking the things on the tray, and picking up the glass of orange juice

Harold (*to Jean, sotto voce*) That the housekeeper?
Jean (*whispering*) Mrs Treshunt. Fondly known as Treasure. (*She grimaces*) Though she's more like Mrs Danvers in my opinion.
Harold (*puzzled*) Who?
Jean The housekeeper in *Rebecca*.
Harold Sorry?
Jean It's a book by Daphne DuMaurier.
Harold Never read it, I'm afraid. So what's she do, this Mrs Danvers?

Brenda comes back into the room with the tray

Brenda She goes mad and burns the house down. (*She moves to the doors* L) And don't think I've not considered her example. Ten minutes.

Brenda exits

Harold (*dismayed*) Oh my God. She heard us.
Jean (*ruefully*) I think she's half bat. She could hear a woodlouse wearing carpet slippers. (*She grins*) Good job she's not the vindictive type. She'd have poisoned me by now.
Harold Do you not get on with her, then?
Jean (*amused*) Treasure? Of course I do. We couldn't run this place without her. She's been with us since Henry the Eighth was alive. God knows what'll happen when she goes.
Harold (*curiously*) Is it true she laid into a burglar, once? I did hear the story.
Jean Laid into him? (*Giggling*) She damn near *killed* him. Don't ever confront her when she's close to a proverbial blunt instrument. It'll be more than your life's worth. Half a dozen of her during World War Two, and it wouldn't have lasted six years, I can tell you.
Harold So what exactly did she do to him?
Jean (*shrugging*) No idea. Except it was rather painful, and not the kind of thing one discusses in polite society. It happened before I was born. And long before the political correctness idiots passed the Protect the Criminal Act. Otherwise she'd have been in the dock for rearranging his gender. As it was, she became a local hero. And still is.

The sound of a raised voice is heard down R

Austin (*off*) No, no, *no*. You can talk ...

The door down R opens and Austin Reeves-Mercer storms into the room, followed by an embarrassed-looking Father Carmody. The former is in his early 50s, forceful, and wears dark trousers, cream shirt, a coloured tie, and a contrasting waistcoat. The latter, who is in his late 60s, wears a dark suit and clerical collar

... till you're blue in the face, but the answer's *still* no. In my opinion, it's nothing short of *sacrilege*. (*He crosses* L)

Father C (*soothingly*) I quite understand your feelings, Austin, but the fact remains, we have no *choice* in the matter. (*He closes the door behind him*)

Austin (*scornfully*) Of course you have a choice. You just don't sell it. (*He suddenly notices the others and looks accusingly at Harold*) Who are you?

Harold (*rising and extending his hand*) Harold Crossley. David's flatmate from London.

Jean (*helpfully*) They arrived last night.

Austin (*shaking hands with him without warmth*) Pleased to meet you. Now if you'll excuse me ——

Father C If you think about it logically ——

Austin (*turning to him sharply*) There isn't the *need* to think about it, Charles. I've made my position clear. For a sacred object to go to auction in a public sale-room is an abomination. It goes against everything your religion teaches and you know it. You can't have items consecrated one day, then deconsecrated the next just because it suits your purpose.

Father C (*patiently*) It's hardly a case of suiting one's purpose. Without the money, we've no way of ensuring the disbursed sister's comfort and health at Bethlehem House. The fees are quite considerable ... as they are at any old people's home.

Austin (*testily*) Then leave them where they are. I'm sure they'd be a damn sight happier.

Father C We haven't that option, I'm afraid. The convent's fabric is sadly in need of repair. At least two million pounds would be required to restore it to acceptable standards, and with only six of the sisters remaining there ... all over the age of seventy ... it's no longer a viable proposition.

Jean (*interrupting*) So it is true? You are closing the Convent?

Austin (*brusquely*) Stay out of this, Jean. It's none of your business.

Jean (*standing*) It is if they're selling the Monstrance. Our family gave it to them. How dare they try to sell it?

Father C With great reluctance, I admit, Miss Jean. But though it is unusual for a monstrance to be sold at auction, it's not unknown.

According to church law, it's standard practice when disposing of unwanted assets.

Jean (*hotly*) Then you should be ashamed of yourselves. And if it's so unwanted, why don't you hand it back to those who gave it to you in the first place?

Father C (*mildly*) I wish it were that simple. But we do need the money.

Austin (*scornfully*) Oh, yes. A few thousand pounds is going to make a lot of difference, isn't it?

Harold (*nervously*) A little underestimation, wouldn't you think?

Austin (*glaring at him*) And what would *you* know about it?

Harold (*awkwardly*) Well ... it *is* a Borzoletti piece. And one of his fruit bowls sold in New York last year for over three million.

Austin (*scornfully*) Don't be ridiculous.

Father C (*mildly*) It's true, Austin. I saw an article on the internet.

Harold (*apologetically*) And that was one of his lesser pieces. Some Russian paid almost four million for a pair of candlesticks, three years before. It's in the new book by Thompson and Valderman.

Austin (*to Father C, bitterly*) So that's what it's really about, is it? All this malarky over St Gudrun's falling down is smoke and mirrors. (*Accusingly*) You're trying to cash in on the get-rich-quick wagon, and need an excuse to dispose of the Borzoletti without being too obvious.

Father C (*tiredly*) Of course we want the best price for it. The church has many needs and most of the unwanted items from St Gudrun's have already been sold to provide them. The Monstrance is the jewel in its crown. Its sale will ensure the sisters will be well provided for, and the remaining money will aid the poorer parishes and missions overseas.

Austin (*tightly*) It may have escaped your attention, Charles, but for the past twenty years or so, that particular piece of plate has brought more tourists to Redston, hoping for a glimpse of it, than your precious church did in five hundred years. If it hadn't been for television and *The Antiques Road Show*, we'd have died on our feet like almost every other village in the country is doing. Getting rid of the Monstrance is not an option. If that goes, Redston's finished. And as for us, we may as well call in the bailiffs, knock this place down, and sell the site to build affordable housing. (*He scowls*) Providing anyone'll want it, seeing as there'll be no work available.

Father C I think you're overreacting, Austin. Even without the Monstrance ——

Austin (*cutting in*) You don't see it, do you? No monstrance ... no tourists. No tourists ... no income. No income ... no Redston. It's as plain as the nose on your face. (*He speaks more reasonably*) Look ... If the church is so desperate for funds, then why not put it on permanent display and make a charge for seeing it? Like the *Mappa Mundi* in Hereford?

Father C We couldn't possibly.

Austin (*annoyed*) Of course you could. You just don't want to. (*Fuming*) If I had the money, I'd buy the thing myself. God *knows* what'll happen to it if it goes up for auction.

Harold At least it won't be melted down. According to the book, it'd only be worth a few thousand in real terms ... cost of the gold and jewels, etc. It's the name that collectors'll pay for. There's only a handful of known pieces in the world, and they're all in museums or private collections.

Jean (*bristling*) I don't care where they are. The Monstrance belongs in Redston, and that's where it's staying. When Sir Martin donated it to the Convent, his intention was that it would stay there forever. It'll leave this village over my dead body.

She turns angrily and hurries out of the room

There is an awkward silence. Unsure what to do, Harold sits again, trying to be invisible

Father C (*uncomfortably*) I'm afraid your daughter's reaction is much the same as many of my own parishioners. Such items are treated with great reverence in our faith, and it's a shame to see one offered at a public auction. But we truly have no choice. It has to go. Which is why I came to see you this morning.

Austin (*letting out a deep sigh*) It's not your fault, I know. You're only following orders. (*Moving* L) It's just that it's all been a bit of a shock. If I'd known about it earlier ... I might have been able to arrange something.

Father C It was only discussed last week. At the Cardinal's meeting with Bishop Logan.

Austin (*turning to him*) But you must understand how we feel about it. It's part of our family history.

Father C Which is why I wanted to tell you personally. The Reeves-Mercers have been good friends to the Mother Church ... despite our religious differences. We didn't want you to feel we'd done this without considerable deliberation.

Austin (*heavily*) No. Of course not. (*Resignedly*) I'll see you out, shall I? (*He turns* L)

Father C (*hesitantly*) There is another thing.

Austin (*disinterestedly*) Yes? (*He turns back*)

Father C I understand provenance counts for quite a lot in cases like this, and I wondered if ... well ... if you have any paperwork relating to its purchase?

Austin (*blankly*) Paperwork?

Father C Confirming the Monstrance is indeed the work of Teodoro Borzoletti.

Austin (*frowning*) Well, of course it's his work. Who else's would it be? Half the world could recognize it. It's been photographed more times than I have.

Father C (*mildly*) Twice, actually. Once in ninteen-fourteen at the request of Cardinal O'Keefe, and again in nineteen fifty-two ... which is the print they've reproduced ever since. But that's all beside the point. A letter or receipt from Sir Martin, or perhaps Borzoletti himself —— ?

Harold (*interrupting*) He couldn't write.

Both look at him, suddenly remembering that he is there

(*Embarrassed*) Borzoletti. He couldn't write. Or *read*, for that matter. (*Lamely*) Sorry. It's none of my business. I — er — I'll go look for David. (*He rises and makes to exit* L)

Austin (*suddenly*) No. No, it's all right. The whole village'll be embroiled once the news gets out. And at least you seem to know what you're talking about. (*To Father C*) Well, I'm sorry to disappoint you, Charles. There's nothing in *our* archives at all. I'd have thought the convent held all the relevant details.

Father C (*ruefully*) Most likely it did. But the repository was destroyed by fire in eighteen forty-two and many of its contents were lost to us. (*To Harold*) One of the sisters perished through trying to save what she could, so all we know of the Monstrance's origins came down to us verbally.

Austin Then you probably know as much as *we* do.

Father C (*sighing*) Ah, well. We'll just have to rely on Dr Jones's authentication.

Harold Indiana Jones.

They both look at him

I mean ... Sylvia Jones. From the British Museum? (*Explaining*) We call her Indiana because of Harrison Ford. You know. *Raiders of the Lost Ark*, et cetera.

Austin (*curious*) You *know* this woman?

Harold Well ... not personally. But I have seen her. She does occasional work for Steadman and Waterfield ... the company I work for ... and *they* think she's the bee's knees. She's got a huge reputation.

Austin (*to Father C*) And you're taking the Monstrance to her for authentication?

Father C Not exactly. She's coming down here. To Redston Village. We're expecting her later today.

Austin (*disgustedly*) Nothing like a *fait accompli* to prevent objections, is there? I'm surprised you decided to tell me before the sale went through. Still ... now we know how things stand, it does mean we no longer have to carry on with our yearly donation to St Gudrun's. With three or four million in your coffers, you won't even miss our pittance.

Father C (*protesting*) Hardly a pittance, Austin. Without your family's support over the past two hundred years, we'd have been in a sorry state.

Austin (*coldly*) I only hope you'll return the gesture if we lose Redston Hall. Which is quite possible considering our present financial position. We might well be in the hands of the National Trust by the end of the year.

Father C (*stunned*) I'd no idea.

Austin (*bitterly*) Of course you hadn't. We don't broadcast our problems in the way some people do. But the truth of the matter is, without tourists here, we're finished. And if the Monstrance ends up in a private collection somewhere on the other side of the world ... (*He throws up his hands*)

Brenda enters the room through the main doors

Brenda (*heavily*) Mrs Vale and her daughter.

Austin (*turning to her*) What?

Brenda They've just arrived. And not sounding too happy.

Austin (*sighing*) Are they ever? What is it this time? Not the hunt, again?

Brenda Something to do with the convent, as far as I can make out. They're practically foaming at the mouth.

Austin (*frowning*) Convent? (*To Father C*) I thought this was all top secret?

Father C (*hastily*) It's nothing to do with me. Apart from the sisters and myself, no one in Redston knows anything about it.

Austin Obviously someone did. We may be related, but the Vales and I have never seen eye to eye. If they're baying for blood on account of the convent, it has to be connected to the sale of the Monstrance.

Father C It can't possibly be.

Brenda (*patiently*) Do you want me to show them through?

Austin (*thinking furiously*) Ask them to wait in the Morning Room. Tell them I'm on the phone or something. Talking business. And for God's sake don't let them know Charles is with me. They'll tear him limb from limb.

Brenda exits again

Father C (*mildly amused*) A slight exaggeration, I hope?

Austin (*scowling*) Not if you know them like I do. Marcia Vale's a direct descendant of Edmund Reeves, Sir Martin's brother, and still believes the Redston Estate would have gone to them if Martin hadn't married Catherine Mercer, instead of remaining a widower. Even more to the point, in her eyes, almost half the Reeves fortune was squandered on a piece of religious bling, for the benefit of the Catholic Church ...

Father C opens his mouth to speak but Austin slightly raises his voice and continues

... which she hates with far more fervour than she hates me for inheriting this place. (*Resuming normal tones*) If you'll take my advice, keep well clear of Marcia Vale *and* her obnoxious daughter.

Father C In that case I'd better be off. I'm meeting Miss Jones around half eleven.

Austin I should take the terrace route. (*Indicating it*) We're not open to visitors today, so there's less chance of being accosted.

Father C makes for the terrace, followed by Austin. Harold moves uneasily and unobtrusively down L

And Charles?

Father C halts and looks at him

I'd appreciate it if you'd let me know what her valuation is? Just out of curiosity.

Father C (*doubtfully*) I'm not sure I —— (*Reconsidering*) Yes. Of course. I know I can rely on your discretion.

He goes on to the terrace. Marcia's voice is heard, off L

Marcia (*off*) I will not be treated like a visitor in what should rightfully be my *own* residence

Austin (*to Father C, urgently*) Down the steps and keep to the right.

Father C hurries off R *and vanishes*

Brenda (*off*) I've already told you. He's busy.

Marcia Vale marches angrily into the room, followed by her daughter, Iona, and Brenda. Marcia is in her 70s and a veritable Grand Dame in the Lady Bracknell mould who firmly believes that even royalty are on

*a far lower social scale than herself. She appears very well preserved,
is impeccably made-up and coiffured, and is dressed in a style that
removes years from her actual age. She can produce fake charm when
it is required, but has a viperish tongue most of the time. She carries
a handbag containing a small bottle of pills, etc. Iona is in her 40s,
and a younger version of her mother, but charm has no place in her
life. She is attractive, but her face is a porcelain mask concealing
repressed anger*

*They do not see Harold as they move towards Austin. Brenda remains
by the doors*

Austin (*turning to them*) Marcia. Iona.
Marcia (*frostily*) I was *told* you were in a *meeting*.
Austin Which is perfectly true. And one that may last for the rest of the
day. (*To Brenda with a smile*) It's all right, Brenda. They won't kill me
in front of a witness.

Brenda glowers and exits

Marcia (*sharply*) Witness?
Austin (*indicating Harold*) My new advisor from London. Mr Crossley.

Harold looks surprised as the two women turn sharply to see him

(*To Harold*) Marcia Vale, and her charming daughter, Iona.

Iona gives Harold a speculative look

Harold (*to them, uncertainly*) Pleased to meet you.
Marcia (*ignoring him and turning back to Austin*) An advisor? Then I
take it you *have* heard? And, we, of course, are the last to be informed.
Austin Informed about what? (*He turns away and moves down* R)
Marcia (*tight-lipped*) You know perfectly well, Austin. The attempted
theft of our most valuable family asset by the Roman Catholic Church.
Austin (*looking puzzled*) Theft?
Iona (*sharply*) Of course it's theft. What else could it be? The
Monstrance belongs to us.
Austin (*pretending to realize*) Ahhh. The *Monstrance*.
Marcia (*fuming*) And you can wipe that innocent look off your face,
Austin. Did you think we wouldn't find out? That we'd sat back all
those years and forgotten about it? (*Scornfully*) How little you know
your ancestors. I may be weak in heart, but there's nothing wrong with

my mind. (*She moves down to the easy chair*) Our family has prayed for this day for the past two hundred years, and now it's here, we refuse to be cheated of our rightful inheritance. (*Pointedly*) You have, I hope, reminded them of the agreement? (*She sits*)
Austin (*blankly*) Agreement?

Iona moves to position herself behind the sofa

Marcia (*irritated*) The one between Sir Martin and that ... *place*.
Austin (*mildly*) I'm afraid I'm at a disadvantage, Marcia. I haven't a *clue* what you're talking about. And I am in the middle of a meeting.
Marcia (*snapping*) The importance of protecting our inheritance may well be a matter of little concern to your side of the family, Austin, but it certainly isn't to mine. If you are prepared to be robbed, then that is your decision. We, however, intend using every means possible to ensure our rights are not brushed aside. (*To Iona*) Come, Iona. (*She rises to leave*)
Austin (*hastily*) Just a minute. You still haven't explained this agreement. Agreement to what?
Marcia (*icily*) The return of the Monstrance when that — *place* — was finally closed down.
Austin (*amusedly*) It's the first I've heard of it. Where did that fairy tale come from?
Iona (*acidly*) The fairy tale, as you call it, comes straight from the horse's mouth. I have it in Sir Martin's own hand, and not even *you* can dispute that kind of evidence.
Austin (*dryly*) I'd be interested in seeing it. Even his own descendants have never been certain he donated the Monstrance to St Gudrun's. It's nothing but a family legend.
Marcia (*scornfully*) To you, perhaps. But the Reeves side of the family have always known the truth. (*Balefully*) With very good reason.
Austin So what does it say? This letter. I presume it is a letter?
Marcia (*nodding*) Sent to his brother, Edmund, shortly after his return from Italy, and explaining exactly why he'd done what he'd felt he had to do.
Austin Which was?
Marcia (*flatly*) To make up for fathering Jessamine Mercer's child.
Austin Jessamine Mercer?
Marcia (*coldly triumphant*) His wife's sister. He was *not*, apparently, the paragon everyone made him out to be. (*Scornfully*) Just another wealthy old man with an eye for any Catholic *slut* he happened to take a fancy to.

Austin (*snapping back*) As opposed to the Protestant sluts his *brother* preferred, I suppose?

Marcia (*outraged*) How *dare* you?

Austin (*unmoved*) Spare me the indignation, Marcia. Edmund Reeves fathered more illegitimate offspring than the parson preached about, and you know it. Half the county could claim direct lineage if they felt so inclined. Now stop posturing, get off your high horse, and tell me about this letter you're claiming to have.

Marcia Iona. (*She sits again*)

Iona (*moving down* R *of the sofa with a superior look on her face*) I don't know how much you *know* about the Reeves family history ——

Austin (*sharply*) Far more than you, I'd imagine.

Iona (*snapping*) Then you'd be wrong. As a qualified historian, I've been researching their antecedents for the past few years ... (*Smugly*) ... and discovered a number of *very* interesting facts.

Austin (*witheringly*) I can't tell you how thrilled I am. (*Impatiently*) Now why not cut the cackle, and get on with it?

Marcia (*offended*) If civility is beyond your limited comprehension, Austin, then I fear there's no need to continue. We'll deal with the matter ourselves. (*She begins to rise again*)

Harold (*hastily*) No. Please. (*He looks at Austin*) As Mr Reeves' advisor, I think the more we know about what you've discovered, the better.

Austin (*sharply*) When I want your advice, I'll *ask* for it.

Marcia (*to him*) I thought you were already doing that, Austin. Obviously I was mistaken.

Austin (*testily*) All *right*. But for God's sake give me the shortened version. I haven't time for a lecture on my own family's history.

He moves to the fireplace and glowers

Harold (*soothingly*) Miss Vale?

Iona looks at her mother, who hesitates, nods, and re-seats herself on the sofa

Iona (*to Austin's back*) You may not *want* a lecture, but without knowing the facts, we could lose the Monstrance and find ourselves unable to do a thing about it.

There is no reaction from Austin

(*As though lecturing*) As you know, Sir Martin Reeves inherited his estate from his father, the Earl of ——

Austin (*interrupting*) Yes, yes. And he married Queen Anne's niece who died childless, twelve years later, and if he hadn't married again, his younger brother would have inherited. All ancient history. Now tell me about this letter.

Iona (*glowering*) I'm about to come to it. (*To Harold*) According to documents in *our* family archives ——

Austin (*bluntly*) Which are probably as biased as hell.

Iona (*sweeping on*) In seventeen forty-two, Lord and Lady Mercer ... well known heretics, clinging to the old Catholic religion ... learned that their eldest daughter, Jessamine, had developed tuberculosis ... or consumption, as it was then known ... and was sent to Italy in the hope that the warmer air would effect a cure.

Austin (*turning to her*) Then what's this rubbish about Sir Martin fathering her child? She entered St Gudrun's the following year to give thanks for her cure, and remained there till the day she died.

Iona (*icily*) Have you ever known a case of tuberculosis being cured in less than a year?

Marcia (*smirking*) Especially in that day and age. (*Shaking her head*) No, no, Austin. When she left Farringfield Manor for Italy, Jessamine Mercer was no more consumptive than I am. She was *pregnant*.

Austin (*scornfully*) And that's in the letter, is it?

Marcia Of course not. But it's as plain as the nose on your face. When the child was born, it was left over there and she returned to England to enter the convent because her own family would have nothing more to do with her.

Harold (*puzzled*) But where does Sir Martin come into it?

Marcia (*sharply*) He was the father, of course.

Austin (*amused*) Aren't you forgetting something, Marcia? In seventeen forty-two, Sir Martin was in America. Visiting his plantations. He couldn't possibly have fathered this fictitious child you mentioned. Your precious letter's a forgery.

Iona (*firmly*) I don't agree. I've brought along a photocopy. (*She produces a folded sheet of white paper and opens it. Reading*) "My dearest Edmund —— "

Austin (*caustically*) I *can* read.

Iona (*continuing*) I deeply regret that my marriage to Catherine has caused this breach between us, but since the discovery that her sister Jessamine was secretly delivered of a child of our line before entering the convent those many years ago, my only option was to try and make amends.

Austin snatches the paper from her and looks at it

Austin (*reading aloud*) "Not only to her, but to Lord and Lady Mercer themselves who remain in sad circumstances through no fault of their own, save religious beliefs. To allay the shadow cast upon our own family, and considering we had contributed to their disgrace in no small way —— "

Marcia (*cutting in triumphantly*) You see?

Austin (*still reading aloud*) "I was driven by conscience to offer them an annual sum for the upkeep of Farringfield. And as for my presentation to the nuns of St Gudrun, what matters a few hundred pounds, if one considers the plundering of their holy places since the Reformation? As you well know, most of our estates were once in Catholic hands, and were only gained by us at the cost of their misfortune. In any case, if the rumour does prove true, and the convent is forced to close, I am assured by the Mother Superior that the piece will be returned in secret before the royal commissioners arrive to confiscate its assets and you, in that case, shall share in the profit of its eventual sale. I remain your loving brother, Martin." (*He lowers the photocopy and looks at Marcia*) Is this it? Is this your precious confession? (*Scornfully*) A lawyer would rip it to shreds in minutes. Not once does he admit paternity of Jessamine Mercer's child or donating the Monstrance to St Gudrun's.

Iona (*haughtily*) His gift ——

Austin (*cutting her off*) Could have been anything worth a few hundred pounds. And until the Reformation, the entire Redland estate belonged to the Mercers. No wonder he felt embarrassed at their situation and decided to help them financially.

Marcia (*coldly*) As my late husband often remarked, there are none so blind as those who won't see.

Austin (*snapping*) And as I often say, the devil can quote scripture, if it suits his purpose. (*Dismissively*) Now if this is all you came for, I'll have Treasure see you out. As I said when you arrived, I'm rather busy and haven't time to indulge in other people's fantasies.

Marcia (*seething*) Then our business is concluded. But rest assured, Austin, the Borzoletti Monstrance will never go to auction. And *that* I can guarantee. (*Rising*) We'll see ourselves out.

Austin (*dismissively*) As you wish. Good-morning.

Austin turns and exits DR

Marcia glares after him, then turns to the doors L

Marcia (*imperiously*) Iona.

Iona (*looking at Harold*) Give me a moment, Mother. Mr Crossley and I have to speak.

Harold (*surprised*) We do?

Iona (*pointedly*) As Austin's advisor, there's a few other things you need to know. Shall we discuss them on the terrace?

Without waiting, Iona goes on to the terrace. Harold glances at Marcia in bewilderment, then receiving no response, follows Iona out

They vanish from sight R

Marcia opens her handbag and takes out a bottle of pills. With shaking hands, she opens the bottle, takes two of the pills, then replaces the bottle in her bag and closes it

David enters through the doors L. *He is now dressed in casual wear*

David (*as he enters*) Sorry to have been so long, but ... (*He sees Marcia*) Aunt *Marcie*. When did you arrive? (*He moves to her and dutifully pecks her on the cheek*)

Marcia (*stiffly*) There's no need for that, David.

David (*lightly*) I know. But I like living dangerously. (*He glances round*) Is Io with you?

Marcia (*heavily*) Her name is Iona.

David (*unconcerned*) A rose by any other name ...

Marcia My daughter is not a rose.

David (*remembering*) No. (*Under his breath*) More like a Venus fly-trap. (*Brightening again*) But I'm glad you've dropped by. You can meet my flatmate. From London. I'm taking him on the grand tour, and treating him to lunch at The Dog and Duck. Providing he's got enough cash on him. I'm flat broke, myself. (*Hopefully*) I don't suppose you'd ...?

Marcia stares at him

No. No. I didn't think you would. (*He glances round again*) You've not seen him, have you? He was here ten minutes ago. Crossley's the name. Good-looking chap in his thirties.

Marcia (*disapprovingly*) You're living with your father's advisor?

David (*blankly*) What? (*Amused*) No, no. He's not an advisor. He's a goldsmith. With Steadman and Waterfield in Hatton Garden.

Marcia (*icily*) Indeed.

David Hang on a second and I'll find him. He can't have gone far.

He goes on to the terrace and peers over the edge of the balustrade before coming back into the room

Not out there. Must have nipped upstairs for something. Won't be a mo.

He exits L

Marcia (*furiously*) So. Another of Austin's lies. (*Bitterly*) I *told* her we couldn't trust him. I *told* her.

Iona appears on the terrace and steps into the room

Iona (*briskly*) Mother. (*She heads for the doors* L)
Marcia (*savagely*) He was lying to us, Iona. He's known about the Monstrance all along.

Iona halts and turns to her

Iona Of course he has. It doesn't surprise me in the least. (*Smugly*) But he doesn't know everything, Mother. I've still a surprise or two up my sleeve. The next few days are going to be interesting. (*She gives a satisfied smile*) Very interesting.

Iona exits. After a moment, Marcia follows

As she moves, the Lights fade slowly to end the scene

Scene 2

The same. Early afternoon

The room has been tidied, but otherwise nothing has changed. On the terrace, Jean, now in a light summer frock and wearing sunglasses, is perched on the balustrade top, L *of* C, *gazing* R. *On the table is a tray holding a plate of dainty sandwiches and a glass of wine. Both are untouched*

After a moment, Brenda enters down R, *closing the door behind her and glancing at Jean briefly, crosses towards the doors* L. *About to exit, she pauses, then turns back and moves to the open window*

Brenda Jeanie?

There is no reaction from Jean. Brenda hesitates, then steps on to the terrace

Is everything all right? You haven't *touched* your lunch.

Jean (*dully*) I'm not hungry.

Brenda (*uncertainly*) Do you want me to take it away?

Austin charges into the room L, *carrying a slim document file*

Austin (*calling*) Treasure? (*He crosses briskly towards the door* DR)
Treasure.

*Brenda turns hastily and re-enters the room as Austin opens the door
to exit*

Brenda (*calling*) I'm here, Austin. (*She moves down towards him*)

Austin (*turning to her, annoyed*) You won't believe this, but those
idiots in the Planning Department only want me to —— (*He stops and
frowns*) What's wrong? You look worried.

Brenda (*amused*) No I don't.

Austin Yes, you do. I know that look. I've lived with it for the past fifty
years. Now come on. Spit it out. Who's upset you?

Brenda No one. I'm fine. (*She hesitates*) But if you *must* know ... I'm
concerned about Jean.

Austin Why? (*He sees Jean on the terrace*) What's she been saying?

Brenda (*heavily*) She's not saying anything. That's the problem. She's
hardly said a word since this morning, and her lunch is just as I left it.
I think it's this convent business.

Austin (*frowning*) What?

Brenda (*sighing*) Don't play the innocent, Austin. You know *exactly*
what I'm referring to.

Austin (*reluctantly*) Well ... maybe I do. But it shouldn't concern her.
(*Firmly*) It's not as though *we*'re Catholics. If they have to sell the
Monstrance, then let them get on with it. I'm annoyed, of course. And
have every right to be. But Sir Martin gave it to them, so they can
please themselves what they do with it. Their fight'll be with Marcia.
Not me.

Brenda (*dryly*) So you wouldn't be interested in a million pounds or so,
if the law decides in her favour?

Austin I wouldn't turn it down. Even a million would come in useful,
these days. But it's not going to happen, Treas. I promise you. If the
Vales *do* go to Court, it'll cost them more in legal fees than ever they'd
get out of it ... especially without my backing. Now let's forget about it
and concentrate on more important issues. (*Displaying the document
file*) This planning application ——

Brenda (*interrupting*) You don't think she'll do something stupid?

Austin stares at her

The way she did when her mother died?
Austin (*frowning*) That was ten years ago. She was only a child.
Brenda She was fifteen, Austin. And it could have been serious.
Austin (*dismissively*) Oh come on, Treasure. She only ran away. I did it myself, once. And we were both back in our own beds before nightfall. (*Frowning*) But maybe you're right. I don't want her mixed up with what's going on at St Gudrun's — if that's what the problem is. Leave it with me, and I'll have a word.

Brenda nods, then turns and exits L

Austin glances at Jean and then at the file he is holding, comes to a decision, nods to himself and exits down R, *closing the door behind him*

Jean remains unmoving. After a moment, David's voice is heard

David (*off* R, *calling*) Soft. What bird on yonder coping ... perilously sits? 'Tis Jeanie with the light brown hair, a-combing out her nits. (*Pause*) Hoy. Cloth-ears. Summon the fatted calf. We're back.

Jean does not react

A moment later, David appears R *on the terrace, followed by Harold. Both are perspiring heavily*

(*To Jean*) Hello-o. Anybody home? (*Waggling his hand in front of her eyes*)
Jean (*annoyed*) Get lost, retard. (*She brushes his hand away*) You stink like a brewery.
David (*unfazed and moving to the window*) What's with the Sphinx look? Or is it Humpty Dumpty? Don't get your hopes up if it is. There's not a King's horseman in *miles*. Just a couple of hot and sticky queens.

He enters the room, followed by an embarrassed Harold

Harold I wish you'd stop saying things like that.
David (*moving down to the sofa and collapsing on it*) Why? Worried about the image, are we? (*He yawns, then grins*) I shouldn't bother. Now she's met you, she wouldn't believe you're gay in a million

years. Me, yes. But *you*. No, no, no, no, *no*. You're her knight in
shining armour.
Harold (*surprised*) What?
David (*airily*) Oh, yes. She's got designs on your body, mate. And I
don't mean tattoos.
Harold (*tiredly*) Give it a rest, David. We hardly know each other. (*He
moves to the easy chair*)
David She's a woman, and you're a man. What more do you need to
know?
Harold (*sadly*) No wonder you fight like cat and dog. I'm surprised
she's not throttled you.
David (*earnestly*) Oh, she's tried. She's definitely tried. Got a nasty
streak, our Jeannie. You'd better watch out when she starts fluttering
her lashes at you. She don't take rejection well.
Harold (*dryly*) And what makes you think I'd reject her?
David (*startled and sitting up*) You don't *fancy* her, do you?
Harold That's for me to know, and you to find out.
David (*grinning*) Oh, my God. You *do*. Don't you? You fancy her.

Jean gets off the wall and comes into the room

Harold (*not seeing her*) Do you mind if we change the subject? (*He
sits*)
Jean (*caustically*) Well *I* certainly don't. (*She removes her sunglasses*)

They both turn their heads to see her

(*To David*) I'm not deaf, you know. And for your information, I
haven't got designs on anyone's body. Least of all his. (*To Harold*) No
offence, Harold. But if I'm going to have my personal life discussed,
I'd prefer to be part of the conversation.
David (*grinning at Harold*) You see? A very nasty streak.
Jean (*snapping*) At least I'm not a moron.
David (*lightly*) How very true, dear heart. You haven't managed *one*
husband, yet. Let alone half a dozen.
Jean (*glaring at him*) I said *moron*, pea-brain. Not mormon.
David (*with mock chagrin*) Sorry. (*Brightly*) But it is a puzzle, isn't it?
Twenty-five years old and narry a suitor in sight. What do you *do* for
social life, these days? Line dancing in the village hall, or bingo?
Jean (*sourly*) I don't have a social life. (*She moves* C) And in case you
hadn't noticed, we're not overwhelmed with amenities in this part of
the world. It's not London, you know.

She perches on the R arm of the sofa

Harold It's quite picturesque, though. All the old buildings, and things. I wouldn't mind living here myself.

David You'd die of boredom, inside a week.

Jean (*snapping*) Not if you got your finger out and did what you were supposed to do. It's not as if *I'm* going to inherit, is it? *You're* the heir to the throne. God knows what'll happen when you take over. You haven't a clue what goes on here. The only thing you're good for, is spending money we no longer have.

David (*unfazed*) Up to now. But once we get the Monstrance back, we'll be rolling in it.

Jean (*puzzled*) What? What are you talking about?

David (*patiently*) According to the font of all knowledge over there (*indicating Harold*) if the convent *is* closing down, then they've no option but to hand it back to us. The venomous Vales have some sort of letter confirming it.

Jean (*to Harold*) Is it true? Honestly?

Harold (*nodding*) They were here this morning. Before we went into the village.

Jean's face lights up

David And the lovely Io tried to rape him in the rose garden. (*He sticks his fingers down his throat and gags*)

Harold (*irritated*) No she didn't. She wanted me to keep them informed about any attempt by your father to come to a private arrangement with Father Carmody.

Jean (*frowning*) And what did you tell her?

Harold That I wasn't interested. It was nothing to do with me.

Jean And what did she say to that?

Harold (*shrugging*) Nothing really. Except she was disappointed.

David (*grinning*) I bet she was.

Harold (*hesitantly*) The only thing was ... she didn't *seem* it. I could have sworn she was smiling when she turned away.

David Can't see that, honey-child. She don't smile much, our Io. Only time she shows her teeth is the second before she bites. I'd sooner face a shark.

Jean (*sourly*) It didn't stop you chatting her up at Uncle Jay's funeral.

David You're joking. I was seventeen at the time, and had only met her twice. *She* was doing the chatting. (*Indignantly*) Trying to get me behind the vestry for a grope in the graveyard.

Jean (*scornfully*) Oh, yes.

David Oh, *yes*. I was pretty good-looking, even then. Why do you think I told her I was gay? It was the only way I could get her hand out of my ——

Jean (*rising and moving up* R) Whoa. Too much information. Way too much.

David (*moodily*) She couldn't wait to spread that bit of news around the village. Took months before I could walk down Church Street without getting wolf whistles from the builders. *One* of them asked me out.

Jean Served you right. (*Misquoting lightly*) Hell hath no fury like a desperate woman scorned.

David (*scowling*) And they don't come more desperate than her. Why do you think I moved to London when I finished at uni?

Harold (*breaking in*) And speaking of London ... When are we heading back?

Jean Tired of us already?

Harold (*hastily*) No, no. Just a busy day on Monday, and I want a good night's sleep before I show my face.

Brenda appears R

Brenda Sorry to interrupt, but Father Carmody's here, looking for Austin.

Jean (*groaning*) Not again.

Brenda There's someone with him. A lady from the British Museum.

Harold (*sitting up*) Indiana?

Brenda (*puzzled and shaking her head*) No. London.

David (*in normal tones*) Better bring them through here, Treas. You can serve them tea and cakes while I go look for him. He's not been around for ages. Could be in his study.

Brenda turns and exits

(*Moving towards the door down* R) Do you think they've brought it with them?

Jean (*frowning*) What?

David The Monstrance.

Harold (*frowning*) Why would they?

David (*opening the door down* R) It's ours, isn't it? You said so.

Harold (*awkwardly*) Yes. But they won't know that, yet. Unless the Vales have broken the news.

David (*grimacing*) I wouldn't put it past them. It's probably why these two have turned up. There'll be full-scale panicking in the Vatican.

David exits

Jean (*to Harold*) They can panic all they like. If they've *got* to give it back, then there's nothing they can do about it.

Harold (*doubtfully*) I don't know. Your father seems to think ——

Brenda enters L, followed by Sylvia Jones and Father C. Sylvia is smartly dressed in a light summer suit, and is in her 40s

Brenda Dr Jones and Father Carmody.

Brenda stands by the door as they pass her, then exits

Father C (*distractedly*) Jeannie. Mr ... Crosbie?

Harold (*standing*) Crossley.

Father C (*apologizing*) I'm so sorry.

Harold (*easily*) No problem.

Father C (*indicating her*) Dr Jones, of course, you know.

Harold (*smiling*) Not exactly. (*To her*) I've seen you in the workshop. (*He moves round to her*) At Steadman and Waterfield. I'm one of their smiths. (*He extends his hand*)

Sylvia (*warmly*) I thought I knew the face. I just couldn't place it. (*She shakes his hand*) You're the one who made the masks I saw, the last time I was there? Melpomone and Thalia. Very impressive.

Harold (*remembering*) Oh. The theatre masks. Comedy and tragedy. That's right. A special commission from Dame Agnes. For their golden wedding.

Sylvia (*glancing round*) And this is where you live? In Redland?

Harold (*hastily*) No, no. I'm just a guest. London's my base. St John's Wood.

Jean (*cutting in*) Would you like to sit down? (*She indicates the sofa*) Dad will be with you in a minute.

Sylvia smiles at her, and moves round to sit on the sofa, but Father C remains standing

Is this about the Monstrance?

Father C (*awkwardly*) I'm afraid it is.

Harold (*to Father C*) I was hoping to see it before I went back. (*Explaining*) Being in that line of work. Must be awesome in the flesh, so to speak? (*To Sylvia*) What did you think, Dr Jones?

Sylvia (*carefully*) It's certainly an extraordinary piece. (*Smiling*) And it's Sylvia. Miss Jones makes me sound like a character from *Rising Damp*.

Harold The old sitcom, you mean? Frances de la Tour and what's-his-name? The Reggie Perrin man. (*Smiling*) Bit before my time. Now if you'd said *Bridget* Jones ...

Jean (*interrupting again*) And what do you think it's worth?
Sylvia (*reluctantly*) Well ... It's difficult to say at the minute.
Jean Why's that? I thought you were an expert?
Sylvia (*mildly*) I am. But I need to ask a few questions before making a
decision.
Jean So?

David enters down R

David He's on his way.
Father C (*to Sylvia*) Mr Reece-Mercer's son.
David (*moving to her, hand outstretched*) David. And *you* must be the
famous Dr Jones.

They shake hands

(*In a scary voice*) Welcome to the Temple of Doom. (*Laughing*) What
have you done with "Short Round"?

Harold winces and turns away

Sylvia (*rolling her eyes*) If I've heard that *once* ...
David (*contrite*) I know. I know. But I couldn't resist it. And if you *will*
go round looking for ancient treasure ...

Brenda enters with a laden tray of tea and biscuits

Speaking of whom ...

*She moves in front of Father C and deposits the tray on the table behind
the sofa*

Jean (*to Sylvia*) You said you had questions.
David (*sitting next to Sylvia*) Questions?

Brenda begins pouring tea

Austin enters down R

Austin Sorry to have kept you. (*He closes the door*) I was in the middle
of something. (*He crosses to Sylvia*) Dr Jones, I believe. Austin
Reeves-Mercer. Very pleased to meet you.

They shake hands

(*To Father C*) And to what do we owe the pleasure?
Jean It's about the Monstrance.

Austin throws her a frosty look

Sylvia As your daughter said. It's about the Monstrance.
Austin (*puzzled*) What about it?
Father C (*uneasily*) I wonder if we could do this in private?
David (*puzzled*) Do what? Make a deal for it?
Austin (*heavily*) David.
David (*protesting*) Well it *is* ours, Dad. The letter says so. If the convent closes, they have to give it back.

Father C looks puzzled

Austin (*snapping*) That's enough, David. (*To Father Carmody, curiously*) Is that what you're here for, Charles? To come to some sort of arrangement?
Father C (*still puzzled*) No, no. Of course not.
Jean (*forcefully*) Then why *are* you here?
Austin (*acidly*) If *I* might be allowed to ask the questions, Jean. (*He looks at Father Carmody for further explanation*)
Sylvia (*mildly*) I'm afraid it's answers we're looking for, Mr Reeves-Mercer.
Austin (*slightly irritated*) Call me Austin. I haven't much time for formality. So. How do you think I can help you?

Brenda hands a cup of tea to Father C, then another to Harold who at once offers it to Jean, who ignores it. Brenda picks up two more cups and moving clockwise round the sofa, places them on the table in front of David and Sylvia

David (*surprised*) No cakies?

Brenda ignores him and returns to the tray the way she came

Sylvia (*to Austin*) It really *would* be better if we discussed this in private.
Austin If it's about the Monstrance, I can't see it matters. It's hardly a secret in this house, and if the Vales are anything to go by, the whole damn village'll be discussing it by tomorrow.

Brenda begins to approach Austin with his cup, but he waves her away. She returns to the tray, puts the cup down and picks up the plate of biscuits, offering it to Father C first

Sylvia (*reluctantly*) In that case, I'd better get on with it. As you know ... I've been asked to authenticate the St Gudrun's Monstrance.
Jean (*firmly*) The Borzoletti.

Brenda then offers the plate to Harold, who shakes his head, and she moves clockwise round the sofa to deposit the plate on the coffee table. As she moves away, David grabs a biscuit and begins eating

  Brenda exits L

Sylvia (*hesitantly*) I'm not sure how to put this ... but when was the last time you saw the Monstrance?
Austin (*puzzled*) I've never seen it. Not in real life. None of us have. How could we? It's been inside the convent since seventeen sixty-five.
Sylvia But it *was* donated by an ancestor ?
Austin (*nodding*) Sir Martin Reeves-Mercer.
Jean (*interrupting*) With certain conditions.

Austin glares at her

Sylvia (*carefully*) Do you know how he delivered it to the convent? Would he have taken it himself, or sent a servant?
Austin (*frowning*) How would I know? It's almost three hundred years ago. All I *can* tell you is that he brought it back from Italy, gave it to St Gudrun's, and started a family feud that's been going on ever since. (*Impatiently*) Now would you please get to the point ?
Father C (*uneasily*) I'm sorry about this, Austin, but it's something we have to know.
Austin What is? If you'd stop beating about the bushes and spit it out, we might resolve what's bothering you before the day's out.

Sylvia and Father C exchange glances

Sylvia (*sighing deeply*) Very well. I don't know there's any other way to break the news, but the St Gudrun's Monstrance isn't by Borzoletti.

There is a stunned silence

Austin (*finally*) But that's *ridiculous*. Of course it is.

Sylvia I'm afraid there's no doubt. It's a beautiful example of the goldsmith's art, and the style is certainly that *of* Borzoletti. But it's definitely not his handiwork. All I can suggest at the moment is that it's a very clever copy.

David (*dismayed*) You mean it's worthless?

Harold It'll certainly be worth something. A few thousand pounds, perhaps. (*To Sylvia*) But not millions?

Sylvia (*shaking her head*) The gold's genuine enough, but the stones aren't *top* quality. I'd say it could fetch around three thousand on a good day.

Jean (*sharply*) I don't believe it. How do you know it's not Borzoletti?

Harold (*uncomfortably*) She *is* a world authority, Jean.

Jean (*hotly*) She could still be wrong.

Sylvia (*quietly*) That's true. I have been in the past, and could be in the future. (*Regretfully*) But in this case ... I'm afraid there's no question.

There is an awkward silence

(*Helpfully*) I could arrange for a second opinion if you'd like?

Austin (*heavily*) Would there be any point?

Sylvia shakes her head

(*Bitterly*) So all these years, we've been living with a lie. He must be laughing in his grave.

David Who must?

Austin (*bitterly*) Sir Martin bloody Reeves, of course. Not only has he fooled the Catholic Church for the last two hundred and forty odd years, he also betrayed his wife, brother, and everyone else who've regarded him as being a saint. (*Hollowly*) Just wait till Marcia hears about it. You'll hear her shrieking in Cornwall.

Harold (*frowning*) Not necessarily. It mightn't be his fault.

Austin (*sharply*) Of course it's his fault. Who else's could it be?

Harold I can suggest another possibility.

Jean Oh?

Harold Well ... supposing the Monstrance was genuine?

Sylvia (*protesting*) But I've already said ——

Harold (*cutting in*) When he gave it to St Gudrun's, I mean.

Austin What?

Harold (*looking at Father Carmody*) Isn't it possible that someone in the convent could have replaced it with a copy?

Father C (*shocked*) Certainly not. How could they?

Harold (*hastily*) I don't mean for financial gain. I just mean ... to *protect* it.

Everyone looks at him

(*Apologetically*) I'm not *that* well up in religious knowledge, but after the Reformation, wasn't there some sort of purge against the Catholic Church? Pulling the monasteries down and confiscating their assets, et cetera?

Father C   (*mollified*) True. We were persecuted by most of the population from fifteen sixty-eight to eighteen twenty-nine and had to endure strong religious intolerance. None of our faith, for instance, could hold high office of any kind. The law forbid it.

Harold   And if the state needed cash for some reason, they just took what they wanted from the remaining Catholic gentry and what few churches were left.

Austin   (*dryly*) Not one of Britain's finer achievements.

Harold   So to prevent that happening to the Monstrance, couldn't they have had a copy made?

Father C   (*shaking his head*) I very much doubt it. St Gudrun's has never been a wealthy convent. Had it not been for the benevolence of the Reeves-Mercer family over many generations, it could well have closed down earlier. How would they have found the money to have a copy made? And even if a miracle had occurred, where would they have hidden the real Monstrance? Where is it now?

David   (*sourly*) If they were *that* hard up, they could have sold the original, had another one made and pocketed the profit. Who'd be any the wiser?

Austin   (*sharply*) That's enough, David.

David   (*protesting*) Well why not? He's just told us they were persecuted till eighteen twenty-nine. So if they *did* sell it and have a copy made, it explains why they couldn't put the real Monstrance back after things had settled down.

Austin   I said *that's enough*. (*To Father C*) So. It seems we have another possibility. Either the Monstrance was a fake to begin with, or it *was* real, and someone sold or stole it, and replaced it with a copy. Where do we go from here?

Father C   (*slowly*) I'm not exactly sure. Obviously we've both been deceived ... but when and by who, it's impossible to say.

Harold   (*thoughtfully*) Well if the original was by Borzoletti, it must have been copied after nineteen fifty-two. When the famous photograph was taken.

Sylvia opens her mouth to speak

Jean   (*chipping in*) Or ninety-three. When *The Antiques Road Show* filmed it.

Austin (*remembering*) Of course. (*To Father C*) Did any of their experts examine it?

Father C (*frowning*) They certainly saw it. It's the main reason Redston was chosen for the programme. Most of them went to the convent to watch the filming. But they wouldn't have been allowed to handle it.

Sylvia If I could just say something?

Austin (*continuing*) Would they have needed to? If it was a fake then, how could they have missed it?

Sylvia (*firmly*) The short answer is easily. I'm very familiar with the nineteen fifty-two photograph ... and without question, the Monstrance in St Gudrun's, is one and the same piece. What they'd have seen would have been what everyone's always believed to be Borzoletti's masterpiece. Apart from a handful of experts like myself, who've handled the genuine articles, it would be impossible for valuers to detect a forgery. But if, as Harold's just suggested, a copy was made of the original Monstrance, we do have something to go on. To begin with, it would have been done after eighteen-thirty.

David And why's that?

Sylvia Because until then, Borzoletti's name was hardly known outside Italy. His work was mainly private commissions. The Menari fruit bowl, Tescardi's candlesticks, Pius the Sixth's goblet, the Angelotti peacock, et cetera. He just wasn't a commercial goldsmith. He'd been dead fifty years, before the rest of the world started realizing what a genius he was.

Jean (*doggedly*) You still haven't explained ——

Sylvia (*continuing*) The Monstrance I've just examined isn't some piece of mass-produced tat. It's a work of art in its own right. As I said earlier, it's real gold, the stones are second-rate but still valuable, and prior to eighteen-thirty, it wouldn't have sold for much less than a genuine Borzoletti. It's only after that, he became collectable and prices soared. To make a copy earlier, would have been a waste of money.

Austin (*frowning*) So what you're saying is, even if Sir Martin's Monstrance isn't by Borzoletti, at that time, it would have had almost the same value?

Sylvia Give or take a few pounds. Yes.

Austin (*brightening*) Which would explain why he never actually mentioned Borzoletti in his diary? It wouldn't have meant anything.

Sylvia (*agreeing*) Not outside Florence.

Austin (*happier*) Then putting aside the theory that it could have been copied, there was no fraud intended by him?

David (*disgustedly*) Apart from the story that Borzoletti made it.

Sylvia And that could be a case of wishful thinking, after he'd been "discovered " by the general public. (*She picks up her tea and sips* *at it)* It does happen, you know. Even in the world of academia. To be honest, I had my doubts from the first time I saw the photograph. There's no record of him ever making a Monstrance ... though it's not to say he didn't. So many documents have vanished or been destroyed during the last three hundred years. Ordinarily, I'd have suggested it could have been a piece by one of his pupils, but he was only thirty-one when he died, so it's very unlikely.

David *(disgruntled)* So much for the "Life of Riley", then. One minute we're millionaires, and the next we're digging out the begging bowls again. Three thousand's not going to go far if we've to share it with the Vales.

Sylvia *(puzzled)* I'm sorry?

David Well even if it is a fake, it's still ours, isn't it? We do get it back.

Father C *(frowning)* I don't understand.

Austin *(hastily)* I was going to call you this afternoon, and put you in the picture. There's been an unexpected development regarding its ownership. When the Vales turned up earlier, they were waving a letter from Sir Martin to his brother, indicating that if the convent ever closed, the Monstrance would be handed back to the Reeves-Mercer family.

Father C *(shocked)* But that can't be true. It was donated.

Austin Not according to *that*. It was merely on some sort of permanent loan. They took great pleasure in showing it to me. Whatever it eventually fetches, half the money goes to them. I've a photocopy in my study.

Father C *(concerned)* Could I see it?

Austin Of course. If you'd like to come through? *(To Sylvia)* Dr Jones?

Father Carmody puts his cup on the tray

Sylvia *(reluctantly)* It's none of my business, really. I just came down to authenticate. But if I might look round the Hall?

Austin Of course. David or Jean can escort you. Fill you in on the details. Or if you'd prefer to wander ...?

He indicates to Father C, and they exit down R, closing the door behind them

Sylvia *(rising)* So who's the sacrificial offering? *(She smiles at them)*

David *(moodily)* Better be Jean. She's the official tourist guide.

Jean *(glowering)* I'd rather not, if you don't mind. I'm at it three days a week as it is. It's about time *you* took a turn.

David *(rising)* In that case, madam *(he bows to Sylvia)* you shall have my undivided attention. *(He indicates the doors L)* Walk this way, and

the delights of Redston Hall shall be displayed for your approbation.
(*He glides to the doors*)
Sylvia (*amused*) If I could walk *that* way ... it'd be a miracle.

She follows him out of the room. They exit

Harold (*putting his cup on the tray*) That was a bit rude, if you don't
mind my saying so? It's not *her* fault the Monstrance is a fake.
Jean (*sitting in the easy chair*) I know. But why did she have to spoil
things? (*Unhappily*) For three hundred years it was real to us. Our
family had been responsible for bringing one of the world's most
famous works of art to Redston ... even if we had handed it over to
the Catholics. It was something we were proud of. And now ... now ...
it turns out to be just a glorified bread basket that someone knocked
together in his lunch break.
Harold (*taken aback*) It's nothing of the kind. You heard what she said.
It's still a valuable piece of work.
Jean (*hotly*) But it's not worth millions, and that's what we need to save
Redston Hall.
Harold (*frowning*) Are things really that bad?
Jean (*gloomily*) They're ten time worse in my opinion. Dad doesn't tell
me everything, but I know we're in deep financial trouble.
Harold (*kindly*) I wish there was something I could do.
Jean You can leave me alone for a few minutes. Give me time to snap
out of the mood I'm in. I've been a real bitch these last few days, and
this afternoon's revelations haven't exactly helped. I might even burst
into tears.
Harold I don't suppose it'll solve anything, but as my sister always
says, it certainly makes you feel better. I'll take a stroll in the garden,
if that's all right?

Jean nods

Harold exits on to the terrace and vanishes L

*Jean sits there, a picture of misery. After a moment, Marcia's voice is
heard off* L

Marcia (*off*) ... Obviously intent on ignoring us. I wouldn't be surprised
if he'd given orders that we weren't to be admitted.

Jean rapidly wipes her eyes as Iona enters L, *followed by Marcia.
Both dressed as before*

Iona (*witheringly*) Oh. So there is someone at home? We've been ringing the bell for the last five minutes. (*She moves behind the sofa*)

Marcia And the door was wide open. Anyone could have entered.

Jean (*standing*) Aunt Marcia. Iona.

Iona (*icily*) I'm sorry if we're disturbing you, but Mother lost an earring this morning.

Jean (*blankly*) In here, you mean? (*She glances round the floor*)

Iona (*scathingly*) We'd hardly be back if she'd lost it in the village.

Marcia (*moving down* L *of the sofa*) It's only of sentimental value, dear. But as you'll agree, one without the other is of no use whatsoever. (*Sweetly*) I wonder if anyone's found it yet?

Jean I can ask Treasure. (*She corrects herself*) Mrs Treshunt.

Marcia Thank you.

Iona And do impress upon her, it's a family heirloom. Not something she could slip into her pocket and forget to mention.

Jean (*sharply*) If you're suggesting she'd keep it —

Marcia (*in mock shock*) Of course not, my dear. Whatever gave you that idea? It's just I'd be *so* upset if it'd gone forever. They were a gift from my late husband. (*She sits*)

Jean (*still seething*) I'll see if I can find her. (*She moves towards the doors* L)

Iona (*with faked disinterest*) Has there been any news, yet?

Jean halts

About the Monstrance? I understand it was being valued this morning.

Jean (*also with faked disinterest*) Oh, yes. Yes. We did hear something.

Iona (*prompting*) Which was?

Jean (*off-handedly*) It's not quite as valuable as some people thought it was.

Marcia (*frowning*) I find *that* hard to believe.

Jean (*innocently*) According to the valuer ... it could even be a copy.

Iona (*scornfully*) Don't be ridiculous. How could it be?

Jean It's not been confirmed yet.

Marcia (*waspishly*) Of course it hasn't. And never will be. This is just another attempt to deprive us of what's rightfully ours. When did she say this?

Jean About ten minutes ago.

Marcia (*snapping*) Then the woman's insane. (*As the thought strikes her*) Unless ... (*Her face tightens in grim satisfaction*) Of *course*. It's all been arranged by the Catholic Church. They knew it had to be returned when the convent closed, but the loss of millions of pounds would be more than they could bear, so they bribed this so-called expert to defraud us. Told her to say anything to stop us making a claim. (*Scornfully*) And how do we *know* she's a genuine valuer?

Jean (*easily*) Harold seems to think so.

Iona (*frowning*) Who?

Jean David's flatmate. From London.

Marcia (*remembering*) Ah, yes. Your father's new "advisor". (*Pointedly*) We didn't recognize the name. He omitted to mention it when we were introduced ... More proof, if any were needed, that today's social skills are sadly lacking. And what is (*scornfully*) Harold's opinion worth? He's only just met her.

Jean He knows of her reputation. And I think that rules out any suggestion of bribery.

Marcia (*snapping*) Rubbish. Bribery's a way of life in the world of art. Look at daubers like Lowrey and Picasso. Do you think anyone would buy their works if sycophants and dealers hadn't bribed the critics to laud them? (*Dismissively*) Of course not. So what makes this Jones woman so incorruptible?

Iona We *know* the Monstrance is Borzoletti's, and nothing will convince us otherwise.

Jean That's fine. But don't blame us when you end up with egg on your face. (*She pushes past Iona and makes for the door*)

Iona (*calling after her*) She can't know everything.

Jean (*turning back*) But she *does* know her Borzoletti, and she — (*She stops speaking, with a look of surprise on her face*)

Iona (*puzzled*) What is it?

Jean (*staring at Marcia*) How did *you* know?

Marcia (*frowning*) Know what?

Jean (*still stunned*) And who told her? (*She realizes*) Oh, my God. (*Scornfully*) Of all the dirty tricks. We should have expected it, shouldn't we? Since when have the Vales played fair? (*Glowering*) But you won't get away with it. I'll see to that right now.

She turns and quickly exits

Iona (*to Marcia*) What was all that about?

Marcia (*slightly alarmed*) She couldn't have guessed, could she? (*She clutches at her chest*)

Iona (*scornfully*) Of course not, Mother. How could she?

Marcia (*concerned*) Then what was she talking about? (*She fumbles in her bag for her pills*)

Iona I've no idea.

Marcia (*producing the bottle*) But something alarmed her. Go after her, Iona. Listen to what she's saying. (*Urgently*) Hurry.

Iona quickly exits L

(*To herself*) We can't fail now. Not when we're so close. (*She quickly takes two more pills*) It's ours and we're going to have it. (*She recaps the bottle and puts it away*)

Austin enters down R *leaving the door open*

Austin (*surprised*) Marcia. I didn't know *you* were here.
Marcia (*smiling falsely*) A lost earring. (*She touches her ear*) Iona's just enquiring.
Austin (*crossing to the doors* L) Then I'll leave you to it. I need to speak to someone.
Marcia (*hastily*) And I need to speak to *you*.
Austin (*turning to face her*) If it's about the Monstrance, it'll have to be later. I'm having someone take a look at that photocopy you left behind.
Marcia (*coolly*) Really?
Austin There isn't a hope in hell that letter's genuine.
Marcia If that's what you wish to believe, then who am I to stop you? But remember this, Austin. *My* side of the family have always been historians. When it comes to the Reeves' lineage, *our* documentation is far more comprehensive than that of your own. We have many letters sent to Edmund by his traitorous brother, and I assure you, examination of them will prove without a doubt that Sir Martin wrote it.
Austin (*grimly*) We'll just have to see, won't we?

There is a loud scream from Jean, off L, *followed by a series of heavy crashes and the shattering of earthenware. Both of them react and turn towards the doorway*

Iona (*off*) Oh my God.

Austin dashes out into the hall

Austin (*off*) Jean? (*Alarmed*) *Jean?* Quick. Someone call an ambulance. *Move.*
Brenda (*off* L) What's happened? What is it? (*A muffled gasp*)
Iona (*off*) Is she all right?
Austin (*off*) Don't touch her. (*Wildly*) Is anyone calling an ambulance?
David (*off*) Jeannie? What's happened?
Austin (*off*) Stay where you are. Don't come any closer.

Father C appears in the doorway down R

Iona (*off*) She fell down the stairs. I saw her falling.
Austin (*off*) Give her some air. Give her some air.
Brenda (*off*) She's not breathing, Austin. She's stopped breathing.
Austin (*off*) Jeanie. (*Distraught*) Jeanie.

Harold hurries into view on the terrace R, *and enters the room as the offstage babble continues*

Harold (*to Marcia, breathlessly*) What's happened? What's all the noise? (*He glances at the doorway* L)
Marcia (*shaken*) There seems to have been an accident.
Harold (*blankly*) Is someone hurt?

Sylvia enters the room unsteadily

Sylvia (*dazedly*) It's Miss Reeves-Mercer. I think she's *dead*.

Harold dashes out

Sylvia and Marcia look at each other. Father C hurriedly crosses to the doors L

The Lights fade rapidly to end ACT I

ACT II

SCENE 1

Mid afternoon, ten days later

The room is unchanged, but the tea things have been removed and the flowers have been replaced with a far more subdued arrangement. Outside, the sky is heavy-looking and faint rumbles of thunder may be heard occasionally. As the scene progresses, the light gradually fades and distant lightning flickers. Austin, in dark trousers and waistcoat, white shirt and black tie, stands by the windows, C, a glass of whisky in his hand, gazing out on to the terrace. After a moment, Brenda enters L, also wearing dark clothing. She sees him and halts

Brenda (*quietly*) Austin?

There is no response

(*After a pause*) Is there anything I can do?
Austin (*absently*) It's going to rain, Treasure.
Brenda Would you like me to close the windows?
Austin (*shaking his head*) I like the breeze on my face. (*He sips at his drink*)
Brenda (*gently*) You really shouldn't, you know. It never did agree with you, and that's the third you've had since we got back from the inquest.
Austin (*dreamily*) She loved this view, Treasure. Couldn't get enough of it. Even as a child, she spent more time on the terrace than she did in the nursery.
Brenda (*soothingly*) I know, dear.
Austin (*turning to her and forcing a smile*) Must have been Gretta's doing. It was her favourite, too. Even in her last weeks.
Brenda (*nodding*) I can see her now. Sitting in her wheelchair, sketching away as though she hadn't a care in the world.
Austin Do you think they're together now, Treas? Gretta and Jean?
Brenda (*firmly*) I'm sure they are. (*She moves closer to him*) Now let me take this (*she takes the glass from him*) and I'll make some fresh coffee.

Austin (*smiling tiredly*) You really are a treasure, aren't you? I couldn't have given you a better name.

Brenda (*raising an eyebrow*) Not that I've always blessed you for it. But it's my own fault for marrying George Treshunt. I should have stayed a Jackson, or picked someone with a name that kiddies could get their tongues round. (*Remembering*) I almost married a Polish man, once. (*She smiles*) Could have charmed the birds off the trees. But I couldn't pronounce his last name, and knowing you, you'd have probably called me Mrs Alphabet. Now sit yourself down and I'll make that coffee. (*She moves towards the doors* L)

Austin (*suddenly*) He was foreign, wasn't he? The coroner.

Brenda (*halting and turning to him*) I couldn't say. I know he wasn't local, but I've no idea where he came from.

Austin Belgium, do you think?

Brenda (*puzzled*) Belgium?

Austin Like Hercule Poirot. Full of little grey cells and bubbling with self-importance.

Brenda stares at him

It didn't suit him, did it? The funny moustache. (*He moves down* R) Looked like a caterpillar under his nose. And all those questions. What were they about?

Brenda (*soothingly*) He had to ask questions, Austin. It's his job.

Austin (*agitatedly*) But he wasn't dealing with a crime, for God's sake. It was an accident. Pure and simple.

Brenda (*protesting*) And that's what he said.

Austin But he didn't believe it, did he? You could tell when he delivered his verdict.

Brenda (*surprised*) No, you couldn't. He was most sympathetic. Everyone said so.

Austin Then why did he go on about her injuries? Wasn't it obvious they came from the fall? The hall table takes two men to move it. And the bowl must have weighed half a ton. Of *course* she had injuries. An idiot could have worked that out.

Brenda is unable to respond

(*Remembering*) And what was *she* blathering on about? Iona Vale.

Brenda (*scornfully*) Oh, you know what the Vales are like. Especially her. Anything to attract attention to themselves. (*Firmly*) She couldn't possibly have heard what she said she did. She was just trying to cause trouble, the way she always does. Forget about it.

Austin (*nodding his head and suddenly changing mood*) Where's David?

Brenda (*slightly thrown*) In his room, I expect. He didn't want lunch, and I've not seen him since the inquest finished. (*She sighs*) It's a shame his friend went back to London. He could do with a bit of company today. I thought he was going to faint this morning. I've never seen him look so pale.

Austin (*frowning*) Do you think he'll get over it? I remember when Gretta died ——

Brenda (*nodding*) Of course he will. He was only a boy then. Now let me get you that coffee.

Brenda bustles out, L

Austin sits in the armchair, a picture of exhaustion

Austin (*after a moment, to himself*) How did she know? How did she know? (*Frustrated*) What the hell did she think she was doing?

David enters L, in dark trousers, white shirt, and dark sleeveless pullover. He looks very pale and has dark half-circles beneath his eyes

David (*dully*) Who? (*Moving down L of the sofa*)

Austin (*looking up, concerned*) How are you?

David (*sourly*) Wonderful. I might just throw a champagne party. (*He sits heavily*) Sorry Dad. I'm fine. Really, I am. (*Curiously*) What was who talking about?

Austin Iona Vale. (*Blurting*) Is the woman completely mad? It's bad enough trying to cope with the accident, but to add to the pain with hints that she might have been pushed, is completely beyond the pale. Who'd want to kill Jean? And why? She hadn't an enemy in the world.

David (*tiredly*) Ignore it, Dad. The coroner did.

Austin (*still irate*) But why did she say it? She knew we could prove she was lying, so what was the point?

David (*dismissively*) She's Iona Vale, Dad. That's the point. If she can't dig up a nice juicy scandal, then creating one's the next best thing. She's always hated us. You know she has. If I didn't know better, I'd suspect her of killing Jean.

Austin (*sharply*) No one killed Jean.

David (*grimacing*) I know. I'm just saying. But if you're so concerned, why didn't you grab her after the inquest and ask what she was playing at?

Austin I fully intended to. But by the time I'd shrugged off the sympathy crowd, she'd gone. Apparently, "poor Mummy"'s heart was playing up again, and she needed to get her home as soon as possible. (*Rising with determination*) I will find out, though. (*He moves towards the door down* R)

David (*frowning*) Where are you going?

Austin To try and get some work done. Bereavement or not, we've still to keep this place running. The hordes'll be back tomorrow.

David (*surprised*) You're not opening?

Austin (*tartly*) Of course I'm opening. We've had no income for the past ten days and we can't run on air. We need the money, David. You, of all people, should know that.

David (*protesting*) But we've not had the funeral yet.

Austin (*firmly*) We can't afford to be closed another week. We have bills to pay.

David We can use the life insurance money ... and what we've got in the trust fund. There's over twelve million in there.

Austin Which only becomes available on your thirtieth birthdays.

David (*hotly*) Or when one of us dies. And Jeannie's dead, isn't she? Jeanie's dead.

Austin (*quietly*) I hardly need reminding of that, David.

David (*contrite*) I know. I know. I'm sorry. (*Pressing*) But we don't *have* to open up the house again. Not till after the funeral. Half the trust was hers. Now the inquest's over, there shouldn't be any problem accessing the money. Think about it, Dad. As a mark of respect to her.

Austin Jean will always have my respect. But with regard to your grandparents' trust fund, if anything happened to either of you, your share would go to the other. You'd both have to die before I could touch it.

David (*protesting*) But surely you can talk to the trustees? It's what she'd have wanted.

Brenda appears in the doorway L *looking hesitant*

Austin What is it, Treasure?

Brenda It's Father Carmody ——

Austin (*shaking his head*) Not now, Treasure. Tell him I'm busy. Too upset. Anything.

Brenda (*reluctantly*) He does seem rather concerned.

Austin (*snappishly*) If it's about the Monstrance, I don't want to know. At this precise moment, I've more on my mind than the ownership of a piece of church plate. Doesn't he know I've been to my daughter's inquest?

Brenda (*soothingly*) I'll tell him you'll speak to him later.

Father C appears behind her, looking rather flushed

Father C Austin. (*Moving into the room and past Brenda*) I know it's
a terrible time for you, but I had no choice. Have you heard the news?

Austin (*with a deep sigh*) Which news is that, Charles?

Father C About Dr Jones.

Austin (*not interested*) Jones?

Father C The valuer you met last week. From the British Museum.

Austin What about her?

Father C She's dead.

The others register surprise

David What happened?

Father C (*unsteadily*) It's just been announced on the radio. She fell in
front of a tube train last night. They've only just identified her.

Austin (*softly*) Oh my God. (*Remembering*) Sorry, Charles. (*Regretfully*)
The poor woman. (*Remembering*) That must have been what the hold-up
was, yesterday. I had to take a taxi.

Father C (*frowning*) You were in London last night?

David We both were. Dad was in some sort of meeting, and I'd to pick
some stuff up from the flat. We caught the same train back. How did
it happen?

Father C They didn't give out details, but apparently it was during the
rush hour. The platforms were rather crowded, and there were several
witnesses who saw her jump.

Austin She committed *suicide*?

Father C It would seem so.

Austin But that's ridiculous. Why would she kill herself? Did she leave
a note?

Father C I've no idea. I only know what I heard. They didn't identify
her until an hour or two ago. (*He touches his temple as though in
distress*) Could I bother you for a glass of water? I'm feeling a little
shaky.

Austin looks at Brenda

Brenda quickly exits

Austin (*moving towards Father C*) You're not looking too good either.
Sit yourself down.

He helps him to the R end of the sofa and sits him

Do you want me to call someone?

Father C (*waving the suggestion aside*) No, no. I'll be fine. Just lack of sleep, overwork, and this business about the Monstrance. It's causing quite a fuss in the upper echelon. They're wanting a second opinion, and all my spare time's been spent in the convent's archives, looking for information. (*Hastily*) But I don't want to bother you with all this. I'm so terribly sorry about Jean.

Austin (*quietly*) Yes. We *all* are. (*Taking a deep breath*) So you're calling someone else in?

Father C Bishop Logan's arranging it with some Italian expert. Though in view of Sir Martin's letter to his brother, I can't really see the point. If it has to be returned to your family, the value is immaterial.

David So when will we get it? In time for the funeral?

Austin (*sharply*) David.

David (*defensively*) It's what she'd have wanted, Dad. You should have seen her face when we told her we were getting it back, real thing or not. It's part of our history. She'd love to know it was in the church for her service.

Father C (*regretfully*) I'm afraid it may be some time before the return takes place ... if ever. Our legal experts have examined the photocopy you made for me, and confirm that as no mention is made of the Monstrance being Sir Martin's gift to the Convent, it could be referring to anything. Until the matter's proved, it will have to remain in the Church's ownership.

Brenda enters with a glass of water

She hands it to Father C who takes a quick sip

Austin (*dryly*) If that doesn't give Marcia a heart attack, nothing will. And what about the auction?

Father C Out of the question, until Bishop Logan's expert examines it. But I fear his findings will only confirm what Dr Jones told us. (*Sadly*) If only I could find something in the archives. You wouldn't believe how much information was lost. (*Almost in wonderment*) You can still smell the smoke, you know. After all these years. I say a prayer for Sister Grace whenever I'm in there.

Austin Sister Grace?

Father C The nun who died in the fire. That anything's known about the early days of St Gudrun's is all due to her. Without the fragments she saved, we'd have nothing. Even the *Adoration* was almost lost to us. (*He sips at the water again*)

David (*puzzled*) What's that?

Father C *The Adoration of the Magi*. The painting she was trying to rescue when she died. It only suffered partial damage and was restored by one of the others at a later date. Rather badly, I'm afraid, though I'm sure she did her best. The documents, however, were another matter. A painting can be replaced, but the loss of the records was catastrophic. Barely anything escaped the flames and, of course, Sir Martin's grandson himself was fortunate to survive.

Austin stiffens and looks wary, unnoticed by the others

David (*frowning*) James Reeves-Mercer? What was he doing there?

Father C (*surprised*) He was one of the heroes of the fire. I assumed you'd know. He's mentioned quite a few times in later records. He was passing the Convent when the fire broke out, and went into the flames several times to save whatever could be rescued. He was helping Sister Grace with the *Adoration*, when the beams came down and killed her. He was terribly burned, of course, and a good many weeks passed by before he fully recovered. (*He sips at the water again*)

David And what caused it? The fire, I mean.

Father C Apparently a violent storm was raging and the whole of Redland took the brunt of it. The village's lower end was completely flooded. With extensive damage. And it was lightning that started the fire.

Austin (*surprised*) Lightning? Are you sure?

Father C (*nodding*) There were several eye-witness reports. It brought down the chimneys, part of the roof and a good section of the north wall, too. Sister Angelica was crushed by falling masonry, but fortunately survived, though never walked again, and after the fire was doused, Sister Roseanne found the chalice and Monstrance beneath the rubble and arranged for their repair. Apart from those strokes of luck, eighteen forty-two was not a good year for the convent. It wasn't, until the following Easter that the Sisters were able to return.

David (*frowning*) You said the Monstrance needed repair?

Father C And the Chalice. Yes. Nothing drastic, I understand. A resetting of some of the displaced stones, and a few dents and scratches removed. A jeweller from London had the commission. (*Defensively*) It was all sanctioned by the Bishop. (*He finishes the water and puts the glass down*)

David And how long were they away from the convent?

Father C (*nonplussed*) I've no idea. A few days. Perhaps a week. Why do you ask?

David (*excitedly*) Because it could explain where the copy came from if the original Monstrance was genuine.

Austin (*firmly*) David.

David (*to Father Carmody*) Do you know who did the repairs? And is the firm still going? (*To Austin*) We could trace it from there, Dad. I could get Harry to ——
Austin (*annoyed*) That's enough, David. (*To Father Carmody*) I'm sorry, Charles. But as you'll understand, I've far more on my mind than clerical history. With tomorrow's opening and the funeral on Friday, I just haven't the time. I'm sorry about Dr Jones, but I do have problems of my own. Perhaps we can meet next week?
Father C (*reluctantly*) Of course.

Austin nods, moves down R *and exits, closing the door behind him*

David (*to Father Carmody*) I am right, though, aren't I? If the jewellers switched the Monstrance ——
Brenda I think we should leave it, for the minute, David.
Father C (*to David, firmly*) It's completely out of the question. Ecclesiastical jewellers have always been beyond reproach. A fraud against the church would have been unthinkable. (*He rises, tiredly*) I'm sorry to have taken so much of your time. I just thought you should know about Miss Jones. (*To Brenda*) It's all right, Mrs Treasure. I can see myself out. (*He moves towards the doors* L)
Brenda (*kindly*) You're sure you're feeling better?
Father C (*unsure*) Quite recovered, thank you. Now it's back to the archives and a few more hours of research. (*He sighs*) Not that it's likely to be of use ... unless St Anthony's in a very good mood.

Brenda looks blank

(*Explaining*) St Anthony of Padua. He's our patron saint of lost things. I find myself appealing to him rather frequently, of late. Whoever said old age was a blessing? (*Nodding to David*) David. (*To Brenda*) Mrs Treasure.

Father C exits L

David (*to Brenda*) I don't know about St Anthony, but if he's forgetting where he's put things, it's about time he retired. He must be seventy, if he's a day. He should pack it in and give someone younger a chance.
Brenda (*dryly*) And that applies to me, does it?
David (*puzzled*) You?
Brenda Well *I'll* not see seventy again. Should I hand in *my* notice?
David (*forcing a grin*) Don't be daft, Treasure. You can't hand in *your* notice. You're one of the family. And besides ... there's not much you

forget. He can't remember your name, and God knows how many times he's been here in the last ten years. (*Scornfully*) Mrs Treasure.

Brenda (*dryly*) And whose fault's that? Your precious father's, that's who. He's not called me by my real name since the day he found his tongue. I've always been Treasure to him, and it rubbed off on you and poor Jeannie, as well. How do you expect him to know my name if he's never heard anyone use it? (*She turns to look off* L, *and cocks her head*) Now who's that?

David (*frowning*) What?

Brenda Someone at the door. Didn't you hear the bell?

David No.

Brenda (*dryly*) You need the wax cleaning out.

She exits L

David gets to his feet and moves up to the window. Stepping on to the terrace, he pulls out his mobile phone and punches out a number. A few moments later his lips begin to move, and he turns his back to look out at the darkening view as he speaks

Brenda enters, followed by Iona, in a summer dress topped by an expensive looking light raincoat and carrying a small folded umbrella

(*Frostily*) I expect it's Mr Austin you're wanting?

Iona (*moving past her*) Not at the present moment.

Brenda (*glowering*) I'm sure he'll want to speak with you.

Iona (*indifferently*) Oh? (*She moves to the easy chair, opening her coat*)

Brenda (*disapprovingly*) What on earth were you thinking of? Coming out with a thing like that at the inquest.

Iona (*depositing the umbrella on the chair*) A thing like what?

Brenda Somebody being on the landing with her. And hearing what she'd said. It was nothing but a pack of lies.

Iona (*acidly*) I don't *do* lies, Mrs Whatever-your-name is. I told the Coroner exactly what I'd heard. Nothing more and nothing less. And I'll thank you to remember who you're speaking to. I don't take kindly to being questioned by servants. Now if you don't mind, you can get back to whatever you were doing, and leave me to have a private conversation with David.

Brenda glowers and exits L

Iona sits in the easy chair and waits for David to end his call. David turns to face into the room, sees her and hastily ends the call before re-entering the room

David (*angrily*) I don't believe it. How you've the nerve to turn up here, after what you said at the inquest. You must be out of your bloody mind. (*He storms down* c)

Iona (*unconcerned*) And what *did* I say at the inquest, David? Simply that she wasn't alone upstairs and I heard her final words.

David (*seething*) Of course she was alone. How could there have been someone with her? We were all down here. We don't have a family ghost.

Iona Be that as it may, she was not alone on the landing. "How did she know?" is what I heard, then she staggered back exactly as though she'd been pushed, and came tumbling down the stairs.

David But you knew damned well there was no one else up there, so why didn't you keep your fantasies to yourself?

Iona (*archly*) And suppress the truth? (*She makes a face*) Not that that idiot coroner showed any interest in it.

David (*sarcastically*) And that surprises you? There wasn't a soul in that room who believed a word you said. Now I think you'd better leave before Dad finds out you're here. I don't think he'd be too happy about it. (*He turns to close the windows*)

Iona (*easily*) Don't you want to know why I'm here?

David (*closing them*) I couldn't give a damn, to be honest. I just want you gone.

Iona (*in mock admiration*) My, my. We are very butch at the moment. Is the boyfriend making a man of you? Must have been an uphill struggle. How is he, by the way?

David (*turning back to her*) If you're referring to Harry ——

Iona Who else? Unless you have other beaux to your string?

David (*tightly*) He's fine, thank you. I've just been talking to him. He's coming down for the funeral. (*Pointedly*) To which you're *not* invited. Now if you've quite finished ——

Iona (*amused*) Finished? I've not even started.

David (*snapping*) Then say what you've got to say and go. (*He sits on the sofa*)

Iona It's about the Monstrance.

David (*sourly*) As if I couldn't have guessed.

Iona (*standing*) I've come to make you an offer.

David (*raising an eyebrow*) Offer?

Iona (*moving upstage*) We've heard on the grapevine. About the valuation. And it seems that it's not by Borzoletti, after all. Just some sort of copy worth only a few thousands.

There is a rumble of thunder

David (*sharply*) Who told you that? It's supposed to be a secret.

Iona (*smiling coldly*) You're not the only one with contacts. But let me continue. As you can imagine, Mother was quite upset. She's always been obsessed with it, and to have it snatched away at the very last moment has almost driven her insane. (*She moves behind the sofa*) So I've decided to rectify the matter. I'm not without finance myself, so when the fake Monstrance is eventually returned to you, I'll purchase *your* family's share of of it ... at whatever the market value ... and the whole thing becomes ours.

David (*acidly*) And if we don't want to sell it to you?

Iona (*amused*) Oh, I think you will. In fact, I'm certain of it.

David And if it turns out your precious letter's a forgery, and the Catholics decide to keep it and sell it themselves?

Iona Then I'd buy it from them. (*She wanders down* R) One way or another, the Monstrance will be ours.

David I wouldn't count on it.

Iona (*casually*) Did you know Dr Jones was dead?

David (*puzzled at the change of direction*) We heard a few minutes ago. Why?

Iona You were in London yesterday.

David (*still puzzled*) Yes. We both were. What about it?

Iona (*smiling*) I was there myself. For Turandot at Covent Garden.

David (*mockingly*) How absolutely lovely for you.

Iona Yes. I'm very fond of Puccini. But it wasn't the only thing I saw last night.

David (*not interested*) Oh?

Iona Interesting places, underground stations. I was on the platform about an hour before the opera began. And guess who I saw?

David I've no idea.

Iona Why, Dr Jones, of course. A little further down the platform and anxiously checking her wristwatch. I was just about to join her, when I noticed someone else struggling through the crowd. (*Pointedly*) Someone I recognized. And someone who positioned himself right behind her.

David (*frowning*) Who was it?

Iona (*archly*) Don't you know? (*She wanders back the way she came*)

David I haven't a clue.

Iona (*smiling*) No matter. But let's just say if you don't feel inclined to sell me your share of the Monstrance, it might force me to tell the police who pushed her in front of that train.

David (*startled*) Pushed?

Iona Oh, yes. It was no accident. I saw everything.

David Then why didn't you tell them last night?

Iona (*lightly*) And miss the opening act? Do you know what those tickets *cost*? (*Dismissively*) And besides ... the woman meant nothing to me. It was only when it happened, I realized it gave me a certain leverage. You *do* see my meaning, don't you?

David I don't see anything.

Iona (*coldly*) Then you're even more stupid than I thought you were. One word from me and the Reeves-Mercers are finished. You. Your father. Redston Hall. Everything.

David (*rising incredulously*) You're suggesting I pushed her? (*Scornfully*) You must be out of your mind.

Iona Did I mention your name? (*She shakes her head*) However, if you're *certain* I made a mistake, there's nothing to worry about, is there? (*She refastens her coat and picks up her umbrella*) My offer still stands. *I* get the Monstrance, or the police receive a phone call. (*She crosses* L *then halts and turns*) I'd advise you to think about it carefully.

Iona exits L

David is left gazing after her. A moment later, he turns and heads towards the door down R, *then suddenly halts. A worried look on his face, he stands there, mind racing furiously. Finally coming to a decision, he turns and heads back towards the doors* R

Brenda hurries in with a small tray holding two mugs of coffee

Brenda (*panting*) He'll be thinking I *am* losing my marbles. I promised him this half an hour ago and what with one thing and another, it completely slipped my mind. (*She proffers the tray to David*) I've brought one for you, as well, now I know Her Ladyship's left. If ever a woman got up my nose, it's that one. Go on. It'll be cold if you don't make a move.

David (*apologetically*) Not for me, Treasure. I'm not thirsty.

Brenda (*concerned*) You've not had a drink since breakfast, and you hardly touched that. I know you're upset, but it's no use pining yourself. We can't bring her back, and she'd not like to see you like this. Try and think of the good times.

David (*shaking his head*) It's not Jean, Treasure.

Brenda (*sharply*) Well I hope it's not something *she* said. (*She glares at the doors* L) She's caused enough upset for one day. Half the village'll be talking about it by now. They should put a padlock on a mouth like hers and throw away the key.

Austin enters down R *carrying a medium-sized, leather bound, and ancient-looking diary*

Austin (*closing the door behind him*) A mouth like whose?
Brenda (*sniffily*) Milady Vale. Why you put up with her, I don't know.
 Your father couldn't stand the sight of her. Till the day he died, he
 swore it was her who'd taken the little snuff box that used to be on the
 music room table.
Austin Don't remind me. If I heard about it once, I heard it a thousand
 times. (*Seeing the coffee*) That for me?
Brenda (*crossing to him*) I'm sorry about the wait, Austin. I completely
 forgot.

Austin takes a mug

Austin It's not a problem. (*He sips at it*) Oh ... that hits the spot.
Brenda (*frowning*) Has something happened?
Austin Happened?
Brenda You seem ... different. More ... relaxed.
Austin I can't think why. (*He takes another sip*) I'm two staff short for
 tomorrow, another bill came in this morning, and there's the funeral to
 get through on Friday. Not exactly an incentive for relaxing.
Brenda I know. But—— (*She breaks off with a sigh*) Best get back
 to the baking. I've done all the scones and Victorias for tomorrow,
 and Jessie'll start on the sandwiches as soon as she arrives. The
 Hardwicks'll do the tours between them, and I can do the brochures
 and admissions. It'll be strange without Jean being here, but we'll not
 let her down. (*She smiles wanly, turns to exit and speaks to David who
 has remained L*) Are you sure you don't want this?

David reluctantly takes the mug

Brenda exits again

David begins to follow her

Austin David.
David (*halting*) Yes?
Austin I need to tell you something.
David Oh?
Austin Perhaps you'd better sit down.

*David looks at him uneasily, then sits on the sofa and puts his untouched
drink on the coffee table*

Have you ever examined the family records? Papers. Diaries, et
cetera? (*He sips his coffee*)

David (*puzzled*) I've glanced at them. Twenty years ago. But never examined them. Gramps kept them locked away as though they were gold, and I wasn't all that interested. Why do you ask?

Austin (*moving up* R *towards the windows*) We're an old family, David. And old families tend to have secrets. (*He pauses for a moment*) The Reeves-Mercers are no exception.

David (*attempting a smile*) You're not going to tell me we're related to the Tombs?

Austin (*frowning*) Who?

David (*shaking his head*) Doesn't matter. They're a crack-pot family of killers in some play I saw the other month. I was only being facetious.

Austin (*drinking coffee as he wanders* L) Until today ... when Charles Carmody came bursting in ... I'd been carrying the secret on my own shoulders. The only person in the world who knew it, and possibly the last in the family who'd have to live in its shadow.

David (*curiously*) What is it?

Austin (*moving down* L) You won't remember your great-great grandfather ... Edward Reeves-Mercer. He died in nineteen fifty-seven. Twenty-six years before you were born. But it was he who found the secret compartment in James Reeves-Mercer's desk ... the one that's now in my study ... and discovered this diary. (*He shows it*)

David holds out his hand for it, but Austin finishes his coffee and puts the mug on the coffee table

To say its contents appalled him would be an understatement. He was so shocked, it caused him to have a stroke from which he never recovered.

David (*uncertainly*) This isn't to do with the Monstrance, is it?

Austin In a way, yes. But drink your coffee.

David I don't really want it.

Austin You're sure?

David nods

(*Picking David's mug up*) Waste not, want not. (*He begins retracing his steps*) To understand what killed Edward Reeves-Mercer, you have to consider what happened after Sir Martin died in seventeen-eighty. (*He sips at the coffee*) Following the Declaration of Independence in America, a huge part of his fortune had vanished. The British government had banned trade between the two countries, and of course, his holding there became untouchable. Napoleon closed the continent to commerce, and Pitt introduced Income Tax to finance the war with

France. By the time Samuel Reeves-Mercer inherited Redland, he was
almost on the verge of bankruptcy. (*He sips at the coffee again*) And
things got worse. The Corn Laws of eighteen-fifteen, and the new
Reform Bills, et cetera, forced him to sell large sections of the estate
in order to keep afloat, and finally he threw up his hands and handed
over the reins to his son James, in eighteen forty-two.

David (*tiredly*) I do know this, Dad. I'm not a *complete* idiot.

Austin (*continuing*) James was forty-seven at the time. Married with
six children, and desperately looking for a way to restore the family
fortunes. Possession of the Monstrance seemed to be the answer. Until
eighteen-thirty, as Dr Jones told us, Borzoletti was unknown outside
Italy, but the Reeves-Mercer Benefit, as it was known then, was now
worth much more than it had been originally. So what James decided
to do was steal it from the convent, sell it, and use the proceeds to put
the family back on its feet. It was all in his diary. (*He displays it again*)
The entire plan. A fire. Replacement of the Benefit with a copy, and
no-one would be any the wiser.

David (*stunned*) So Dr Jones was right. The Monstrance was faked.

Austin (*shaking his head*) No. She got it wrong. We all did. (*He drains the
mug*) After finding the diary, Edward Reeves-Mercer was convinced
a terrible crime had been committed. Not only had his ancestor been
responsible for the convent fire and theft of the Reeves-Mercer Benefit,
but more importantly, one of the nuns had died in the flames. The
family were solvent once more, but their fortunes had been restored
at the cost of an innocent life. For a deeply religious man, it was too
much to bear. He tore out the confession and destroyed it, then had the
stroke that eventually killed him. Only his son knew the truth ... and
that has been handed down to the eldest son ever since. It's the reason
we've continued to donate a yearly sum to the convent, no matter how
fragile our own finances. A form of atonement for what happened all
those years ago. (*He puts the empty mug on the mantelpiece*)

David But you said ——

Austin I know. And if you'll keep quiet, I'll explain. (*He begins to
wander upstage and* L *again*) It was only when Father Carmody told
us the convent fire was started by lightning, I decided to go through the
diaries again and discovered the truth. Until today, we always thought
James had been a victim of Nemesis. His burns were his punishment
for starting the convent fire. But if Edward had looked at the entries
for later in the year ... when James was recovering and writing again
... he'd have realized that the plan was never put into action. A few
weeks before the fire, Peel had greatly reduced Customs duty, and
promised to scrap the hated Corn Laws. It was enough to to stave

off disaster ... and James's involvement with the convent disaster was sheer misfortune. He never went near the Monstrance. He was too busy helping Sister Grace save documents. (*He begins to move* R *again*)

David So it wasn't copied after all? It's still the original?

Austin (*impatiently*) It doesn't matter. The important thing is that James wasn't responsible for Sister Grace's death. He was innocent. We don't have a murderer in the family. (*He opens the diary*) Listen. (*He flicks through the diary, then reads*) ... "Since the night of the fire, those many months ago, I have daily given thanks to God that my foolish plans were forestalled by natural calamity. With cash flowing into our coffers again, our future looks fair, and I consider my injuries fair payment for what could have been a most shameful act against His name." Blah, blah, blah ... "The death of Sister Grace is forever in my mind, but I am told that the Benefit, though somewhat damaged, by the smoke and flames, required only minor restoration to bring it back to full glory." (*He closes the diary*) It couldn't be clearer.

David And what about Dr Jones?

Austin What about her? (*He yawns*)

David Why would she kill herself?

Austin (*frowning*) I've no idea. Financial problems. Stress. Illness. Anything could have triggered her off. (*Curious*) What brought that up? (*He yawns again and sits in the armchair*)

David (*mildly*) You'd not met her before, had you?

Austin (*fuzzily*) No. Why would I have?

David And you've not seen her since?

Austin (*slightly irritated*) What is this? Twenty Questions? I've not set eyes on her since Jeannie's ... accident. (*He leans back and his eyes close*)

David (*after a slight pause*) So you didn't run into her yesterday?

Austin (*drowsily*) I've just told you. I wouldn't have recognized her if I had. (*He yawns*) And I'd other things on my mind. (*Very sleepily*) She'd have been just another face.

David (*puzzled*) Dad? (*Concerned*) Are you all right?

Austin (*without opening his eyes*) Tired, that's all. Up at the crack of ... dawn.

There is a few seconds of silence and lightning flickers

David Dad?

There is no response

Dad?

David rises and moves to Austin's side. Taking the diary from him, he stands looking at it thoughtfully, then turns and exits down R, closing the door behind him

Thunder sounds but Austin sleeps on

A moment later, Brenda enters L. She wears a light raincoat and a hat. Crossing to Austin she looks down at him

Brenda (*softly*) Austin?

There is no response

Can you hear me, dear?

There is still no reaction, so she gently lifts his eyelid. Satisfied, she straightens again and glances round. Seeing the mug on the coffee table, she crosses to it, looks inside, and smiles. Thunder sounds again and she moves to the window to gaze into the darkness before turning to look at Austin again

I shouldn't be long, but you don't have to worry. It'll all be taken care of. Just you get your rest and leave everything to me. (*She produces a large kitchen knife from her pocket and looks at it thoughtfully*) I think this'll do the trick, don't you?

She replaces the knife in her pocket, then exits L

A great crash of thunder shakes the room. The Lights fade slowly to end the scene

SCENE 2

Late morning. The following day

Once more the sky is overcast. The french windows are closed and the room is unoccupied. The two coffee mugs have been removed, the room generally tidied, but otherwise, everything is the same

After a moment, David enters L, in a warm-looking sweater and dark trousers. He is followed by Harold, who wears a dark overcoat over his dark suit

David (*as he enters*) ... Supposed to be opening at eleven, but I can't see them beating a path to the gates if this keeps up. (*He crosses* R) It's the first break since half seven this morning and there's more to come if you believe the forecast. Did you notice the river? It's almost bursting its banks.

Harold Not surprising after last night's downpour. (*Unfastening his coat and draping it on the sofa back*) And it's not warm either, considering the month. (*He hesitates*) How's your dad?

David Like a bear with a sore head. Which he's probably *got*, anyway.

Harold looks puzzled

(*Explaining*) Dropped off in the chair yesterday afternoon. Couldn't bring him round at all, and almost had to carry him upstairs.

Harold Did you call the doctor?

David (*dismissively*) It was nothing serious. Just overtired. He's hardly slept a wink since Jean died. Or eaten, for that matter. None of us have. He was out like a light till this morning, then woke up with the mother of all headaches. (*Wryly*) Been hitting the paracetamol since first thing. (*Waving at the sofa*) Sit down.

He sits in the easy chair as Harold moves round to sit on the sofa

So how'd you get the time off to come down here? We weren't expecting you till Friday.

Harold They owed me a few days and I thought you could do with the support.

David (*wryly*) You sound like a walking jockstrap.

Harold (*giving a faint grin*) But how's it going? Honestly? You seemed really depressed on the phone.

David (*wryly*) Not half as depressed as I was a few minutes later. I had a visit from the lovely Iona. Teeth and claws all sharpened for attack. As usual.

Harold I wouldn't have thought she'd've dared. Not after what you told me she said at the inquest. Are you sure you didn't get it wrong?

David (*shaking his head*) We all heard her. She followed Jean out of here, and heard her upstairs, yelling at someone.

Harold Who was it?

David (*derisively*) She claimed she couldn't see. They were both out of sight ... somewhere in the corridor. Supposedly she was just on her way up there when Jeannie came staggering backwards and toppled down the stairs. All lies, of course, because we know the rest of us were all down here.

Harold (*puzzled*) So what was the point? Why make up a story no one's going to believe? I mean ... "How did she know?" What's that supposed to mean?

David Haven't a clue. Not that it matters. The coroner just ignored it. He'd heard all the other evidence, and knew she was making it up for effect. But you can imagine how we felt.

Harold (*sighing*) I wish I could have been there.

David You couldn't have done anything. Or said much. It's not as though you'd've had anything to add. Anyway ... it was all put down as a tragic accident.

Harold I'm still surprised she showed her face here. What did your father say?

David He wasn't around, thankfully. But the reason she surfaced from the swamp she lurks in was to see me. She brought along an offer to buy our share of the Monstrance ... real or not ... and thought she'd try a little blackmail at the same time?

Harold (*in disbelief*) Not —— ?

David (*amused*) Oh, *no*. She gave up with the sex thing, years ago. She still thinks I'm gay.

Harold (*nodding*) Me too. Ever since she tried her luck the day I met her, and turned her down.

David (*surprised*) You're joking. Why didn't you *say* something?

Harold (*grimacing*) Didn't want to cause embarrassment. First time visitor, and all.

David So what happened?

Harold You don't want to know. But I told her I wasn't interested. In her *or* her proposition. The Monstrance was none of my business and I was staying well out of it. (*Grimacing*) And speaking of that ... You've heard about Dr Jones?

David Father Carmody told us yesterday.

Harold (*shaking his head*) I can't believe it. I was meeting her for coffee that evening. To show her my latest designs. Waited over an hour in Leicester Square, but she never turned up. (*Puzzled*) Why would she kill herself?

David She didn't. According to Iona, she was murdered.

Harold (*startled*) What?

David She claims to have been on the platform when it happened. Just fighting through the crowd to speak to her, and actually saw the killer.

Harold (*stunned*) Did she tell the police?

David (*disbelievingly*) Apparently, she was in a hurry to get to the opera. But the more I think about it, the more I think she was lying. She *couldn't* have seen anything.

Harold Why not?

David She said she recognized her. (*Earnestly*) But how could she? They never met. Not here, anyway. And I can't see their paths crossing anywhere else. Anyway, like I said, she came here to blackmail me. If we don't let her have the Monstrance, she tells the police one of us did it.

Harold (*in disbelief*) And they'd believe her? (*Laughing*) I don't think so. You're so cack-handed, if you tried to push someone under a train, you'd end up there yourself. They could ask anyone. You're not safe to be let loose. And why would either of you kill Jonesie? You'd never even heard of her before she turned up here. (*Seriously*) Had you?

David (*scornfully*) Do we seem the type to spend what free time we have rambling round museums? I've seen enough of this place to last me a lifetime, and Dad's got enough on his plate, trying to stop the government taking it from him. He was in a meeting all afternoon, the day it happened.

Harold Then there's nothing to worry about. Let her say what she likes. (*Changing the subject*) So apart from that ... now I'm here, is there anything I can do to help? (*Hastily*) But not showing the visitors round. I don't think I'm up to guided tours as yet.

David All taken care of, as far as I know. (*Thoughtfully*) Though there is one thing. We found something in one of the old diaries yesterday ... and it's got me a bit puzzled.

Harold (*curiously*) What is it?

David Have a look for yourself. It's up in my room. It *seems* straight-forward, but there's something niggling me and I can't let it go. I was up half the night trying to figure it out.

Harold Sounds fascinating. But why me? I'm not a historian.

David No, but it's something in your line. (*He stands*) Want to come with me?

Harold Why not? (*He rises*)

Austin enters L and sees them. He is wearing dark green trousers, a thick sweater over a white shirt, and a sleeveless jacket

Austin (*giving a forced smile*) Harry. (*He moves to him and they shake hands*) We weren't expecting you so soon.

Harold (*hastily*) I hope I'm not ——

Austin (*gruffly*) No, no. As long as you don't mind fending for yourself. We're opening the Hall at eleven, and we're a bit short-handed, so we'll not have much time for socializing. (*To David*) I'll need you to see to admissions, David. Treasure's not feeling too good. She had a tussle with one of the carving knives, and lost. And if this bloody headache doesn't clear soon, one of the Hardwicks'll have to take over from me. (*Ruefully*) Maybe I shouldn't have opened.

Harold Nothing serious, is it? With Mrs Treshunt?

Austin I don't think so, though she won't let me take a look at it. She's swathed it in more bandages than the mummy in the Egyptian room. (*Reluctantly*) But I am starting to worry about her. She's nearly eighty ... despite her claims to the contrary ... and she can't go on forever. I just hope she'll decide to retire before we have to give this place up. The shock'd finish her off. I think she loves it more than *we* do.

Harold (*hesitantly*) Do you think you will have to sell?

Austin (*heavily*) There's a strong possibility. (*Forcefully*) But it won't be without a fight. Now let me get those blasted tablets before my head falls off.

He crosses down to the door R and exits

David (*glancing at his wristwatch*) Ten to eleven. If we take the back stairs there'll just be time to look at the diary before I have to leave you to it for an hour or so. If you can make any sense of it, I'll be in the entrance hall. (*He moves towards the doors R*) You know where the kitchen is if you want a sandwich or anything, and we don't have the hoi polloi in this part of the house, so no one'll bother you.

Harold picks up his topcoat

Harold By the way ... not that it matters now ... I've picked up more information on the Borzoletti ——

David Tell me about it later. Look at the diary first, then tell me what you think.

Brenda appears in the doorway L. She wears a skirt, blouse and cardigan. Her right hand is heavily bandaged and she is limping slightly. She looks distinctly under the weather

Brenda Father Carmody's on the line.

David (*grimacing*) What does he want?

Brenda Your father.

David Well he can't have him now. The Geriatric Brigade'll be bashing the doors down in two minutes. Tell him we'll call back later. After we've repelled boarders and counted the booty.

Brenda He said it was important.

David And so's stopping this place from falling about our ears. (*He sighs*) Oh, all right. I'll go get him. He's in the study, popping paracetamol.

David exits down R

Brenda (*to Harold*) I didn't know you were back, Mr Crossley. I
wondered whose bag was in the hall. How are you?
Harold (*smiling*) Better than you, by the look of it. How's the hand?
Brenda Sore.
Harold You really should have it checked. In case of tetanus.
Brenda (*scornfully*) Don't have much time for hospitals and the like.
Give me a few days and I'll be right as rain. I'll put you next to David
again ... if that's all right?
Harold Fine.

David enters down R

David Must have gone out through the gallery. Lord knows where he is
now. Do you want me to take it?
Brenda (*shaking her head*) It's your father he wants. I'll tell him to call
back later.

She exits L

David (*to Harold*) You'd better go up yourself. I'd never make it back
before we open now. (*He crosses* L *and up*) But it's on the table under
the window. You can't miss it. I've put a marker in the pages. Tell me
what you think. See you later.

He quickly exits L

*Harold watches him go, almost absently, then stands there, a strange
look on his face. After a moment he turns to exit*

*Marcia enters. She is wrapped in a thick coat, wears hat and gloves,
and carries her handbag*

Marcia (*coldly*) We meet again, Mr Crossley.
Harold (*startled*) Mrs Vale.
Marcia Here to offer more advice, are we?
Harold I'm sorry?
Marcia (*pointedly*) Lying is not an admirable trait in Christian circles.
You told me you were Austin's new advisor.
Harold That's not *quite* true. I was ——
Marcia (*cutting in firmly*) Attempting to deceive me, Mr Crossley. And
if there's one thing I cannot tolerate, it's deceit. (*Moving to the sofa*)

Obviously, the Reeves-Mercers are not similarly inclined. Will you
kindly advise your fellow conspirator that I am here to see him.

Harold He ... er ... seems to be rather busy, actually.

Marcia (*sharply*) I am not concerned with his activities. Obviously the
death of his child counts for nothing. To admit tourists to rampage
through Redston Hall a few days before her funeral, is in my opinion,
nothing short of an abomination. (*She sits*) The man's greed simply
beggars belief. Now if you wouldn't mind ——

Harold (*uncertainly*) It may take a while.

Marcia Then I shall wait.

Harold puts his topcoat down again, and exits L. *Marcia opens her*
handbag and takes out a mobile phone. Peering at it myopically, she
stabs at a number, then holds it to her ear. There is no response

(*Frustrated*) Where *are* you, dammit?

She replaces the phone in her bag and pulls out the bottle of pills.
Removing a glove, she opens the bottle, tips two of the pills into her
palm and swallows them. Replacing the cap, she returns the bottle to
her bag and replaces her glove. For a moment, she sits motionless, then
rises and moves down R

As she does so, Brenda enters L

Brenda (*defensively*) If you're looking for Austin, you needn't bother.

Marcia turns to face her

It's me you'll want to speak to.

Marcia (*coldly*) Why should I?

Brenda It was nothing to do with him. It was all my idea.

Marcia (*puzzled*) What was?

Brenda If you want to bring charges, feel free. All I can say is, I don't
have a second's regret.

Marcia (*dismissively*) I don't know what you're talking about. Tell
Austin I wish to see him at once.

Brenda (*disconcerted*) You mean ... you've not heard yet?

Marcia If you mean about Dr Jone's demise, then of course I've heard.
But I fail to see what you have to do with the matter. She wasn't a
friend of yours. Now please tell Austin I'm here.

Brenda (*thrown*) He's probably in the Long Gallery. We've not seen
him for the past few minutes. He's really quite busy.

Marcia (*scornfully*) My heart bleeds for him. (*Harshly*) If his father were still alive, he'd be appalled at this lack of respect for the dead. And as for being busy, only two cars are in the car park, and those, I strongly suspect, belong to your volunteers. (*She notices Brenda's hand*) Is there something wrong with your hand?

Brenda Just a cut. It's nothing serious.

Marcia Then I suggest you dress it more appropriately. Grubby bandages would never be tolerated in my household. I've dismissed servants for less.

Austin appears in the doorway L

Austin (*fuming*) What is it *this* time? And if it's anything to do with the Monstrance, you can save your breath. I'm not interested.

Marcia (*rising*) As it happens, it's not why I'm here. I merely wish to know if Iona mentioned where she was going when she left here yesterday afternoon?

Austin (*moving into the room looking puzzled*) Left here? What are you talking about? She never came near the place.

Marcia (*taken aback*) But she told me, quite clearly, she was coming here.

Austin Then she must have thought better of it. (*To Brenda*) Did *you* see her, Treas?

Brenda (*reluctantly*) She did come by, yes. But she didn't stay long. (*To Marcia*) Is something wrong?

Marcia (*imperiously*) Of course not. But she failed to return home last night and I'm unable to contact her. I know she had tickets for the National Theatre, and supposed that she stayed the night in London for some reason. The Savoy Hotel, however, insists that she never booked in, which frankly surprises me, as she always stays there.

Austin (*dryly*) Perhaps she's changed allegiance?

Marcia I very much doubt it. We find the Savoy an excellent *pied-à-terre*. And besides ... she's supposed to accompany me to Harley Street this afternoon for my heart appointment.

Austin Then she'll probably be in the station to meet you when the train arrives.

Marcia (*haughtily*) I do *not* travel alone, Austin. My health won't permit.

Austin (*scowling*) It doesn't stop you haunting this place. Well if that's all you came for, I'll get back to what I was doing. We're expecting a group from the The Saracen Hotel in Medlock at eleven-fifteen, but I'm sure Mrs Treshunt can escort you to the door, without you having a heart attack. Good-morning.

He exits L

Brenda (*frowning*) She's not been home at all, you say?
Marcia (*eyeing her with disdain*) I did.
Brenda Not even to change her coat?
Marcia Coat?
Brenda She lost a button. I found it after she left.

Marcia stares at her silently, then slowly clutches at her throat

Marcia (*almost in a whisper*) Iona would never be seen in public improperly dressed. (*Beginning to panic*) Something must have happened to her. I must get back to Ainswicke. Check her wardrobe.

She sways as though about to faint and Brenda steps towards her. Marcia recoils and holds up her hand to stop her

(*Panting*) No. I do not allow servants to touch me. (*She fumbles hastily in her bag for her pills*)
Brenda (*concerned*) Would you like a glass of water?
Marcia (*struggling for breath*) Certainly *not*. I'll partake of *nothing* in this house.

As Brenda watches, she takes two pills and replaces the bottle in her handbag

Just give me a moment to compose myself, and I shall see to my own departure.
Brenda (*frowning*) Shall I call your chauffeur?
Marcia (*acidly*) There's no need for false concern, Mrs Treshunt. I'm well aware of your feelings towards me ... and indeed my daughter. So mark my words ... if anything *has* happened to her, I shall hold the Reeves-Mercers totally responsible.

Turning on her heel, she staggers to the doors L *and exits*

Brenda suddenly sags and supports herself on the sofa

A moment later, Harold enters L *with the diary. He sees Brenda and reacts*

Harold (*concerned*) Mrs Treshunt?

There is no reply and he stares at her

Are you all right? (*He moves towards her*) Mrs Treshunt?

She slowly lifts her head to look at him

Brenda (*faintly*) Austin. Tell Austin.

Harold stares at her again, drops the diary onto the sofa and exits hurriedly

Brenda shakily moves round to sit on the sofa

A moment or two later, David hurries in L

David (*anxiously*) Treasure? (*He sits beside her*) What is it? What's wrong?
Brenda (*clutching at his arm*) Where's Austin?
David Harry's gone for him. What is it? Don't you feel well?
Brenda (*shaking her head*) I'm fine. Fine. It's just something I need to tell him.
David Is there anything I can do? Make you a cup of tea, or something?

Brenda shakes her head again

(*Concerned*) It wasn't *her*, was it? The Wicked Witch of the East?
Brenda (*forcing a smile*) It'd take more than her to upset me. I've still got the ruby shoes, remember? (*Rallying*) Now stop fussing and get back to the door. If there's no one there to take the money, they'll be in like flies.
David No they won't. Mrs Hardwick's covering. She'd just come down for something when Harry gave us the news. (*Concerned*) Are you *sure* you're all right? You're as white as a sheet.
Brenda I'm fine. Really, I am.
David (*puzzled*) Then what is it?

Austin hurries in L, *followed by Harold*

Austin (*anxiously*) Treasure?

He moves down to the R *of her. Harold remains up* L

Brenda (*reassuringly*) It's all right. I'm not about to expire.
Austin (*relieved*) Of course you're not. You're too damned stubborn. (*Sitting beside her*) You said you wanted to see me? Should I call Dr Ellerby?

Brenda (*tartly*) If you do, it'll be *you* that's needing the attention. (*Ruefully*) I'm sorry to pull you away, Austin. I know I couldn't have picked a worse time ... but if it's going to come out, I'd sooner I told you myself. Not let you hear it from a third party.

Austin (*puzzled*) Hear what?

Brenda I should have told you first thing, but I didn't know what to do. I've not slept a wink all night, and if the police come I'll tell them it was my idea. It was nothing to do with you.

Austin (*baffled*) What wasn't? I've no idea what you're talking about.

Brenda Iona Vale. (*Heavily*) I threatened to kill her yesterday.

Austin and Harold react

Austin (*in disbelief*) What?

Brenda I was bringing your coffee through when I heard her talking to David.

David looks disconcerted

It was wicked, the things she was saying. I just couldn't believe my ears. I knew she hated you ... but to tell the police she saw you push Dr Jones under the train was just too much.

Austin reacts

David (*to Austin*) She hasn't done it, Dad. It was just a threat.

Brenda (*firmly*) But she was going to tell them if you refused to sell her your share of the Monstrance. I heard her with my own ears.

Austin But that's ridiculous. We don't even know if it will be given back to us.

Brenda (*quietly*) All the same. I saw red. And I knew I couldn't let her get away with it. The only problem was ... how to stop her? I didn't want anyone else involved. There'd been enough tragedy here already. And then I remembered. The sedative they gave me last year when I hurt my back. To help me sleep. I'd never used it, and it was still in the kitchen. It only took a minute to find it, and add it to the coffee. With you both asleep, there'd be no one to notice I'd gone.

Austin (*staring at her*) My God. So *that's* what ——

Brenda So I took one of the kitchen knives and went over to Ainswicke. I knew she'd go the long way round. Not the short cut through the trees and over the bridge. Wouldn't take the chance of dirtying her fancy shoes. But it didn't bother me. I was waiting inside the bus shelter when she came round the corner. It was raining heavily by that time and she didn't even notice me till I stepped out in front of her.

Austin And what happened ?

Brenda I told her to keep her mouth closed or I'd finish her off, and pulled out the knife to frighten her. (*Ruefully*) The trouble was, the minute she saw it, she grabbed my wrist, twisted it out of my hand and pushed me down the river bank. I thought I'd end up in the water, but managed to stop in time and just lay there in the grass while she screamed abuse at me from the top. I've never felt so stupid in my life.

Austin (*despairingly*) Oh, Treasure. Treasure. What were you *thinking* of?

Brenda (*tiredly*) I know. I think I must have fainted with the pain. It took me ages to climb back after she'd gone. Part of the bank had collapsed, my hand was sliced open, and the grass was like ice in all the rain. By the time I reached the path again, there wasn't a sign of her, *or* the knife. I just lay there bleeding and waiting for the police to arrive and arrest me for attempted murder. But nothing happened. Nobody came. So eventually I picked myself up and made my way back here to change and start the evening meal. I've been expecting them ever since.

Austin (*rising in exasperation*) That's marvellous. Absolutely marvellous. (*He moves down* R) As soon as the news gets out, we'll have the media invading us like locusts. Friday's funeral'll be a bun-fight, and the bloody Vales' ll be in their element. How could you be so stupid?

Brenda mops at her eyes in distress

David (*defensively*) Just a minute, Dad —

Austin (*angrily*) For what? My housekeeper knocks us out with drugged coffee, goes on the rampage with a bloody kitchen knife and I'm supposed to say "There, there. It's nothing to worry about"? Don't you see what this means?

David (*quietly*) It won't mean anything ... if the story doesn't get out.

Austin (*seething*) And how do we stop *that* happening? By appealing to Iona's better nature? (*Bitterly*) Believe me, David, she doesn't have one.

David I know. But there must be some way of keeping her quiet. (*He rises and moves down* L)

Austin (*sarcastically*) And you can think of one?

David (*turning to him*) We can promise her the Monstrance.

Austin looks at him speechlessly

For nothing. (*Quickly*) It'll only be worth a few thousand ... Dr Jones said so. And half of what it *does* bring won't be much use to us ... you said so yourself. She's so eager to get her hands on it, she'll not say a word to anybody.

Austin (*heavily*) And if it *isn't* handed back?

David (*earnestly*) We can cross that bridge when we come to it. The longer we can stall her, the less chance there'll be of anyone believing her. If someone threatens you with a knife, you don't wait months before you report it, do you?

Austin looks at him silently

Austin (*after a moment*) It's worth a try, I suppose ... but it sticks in my craw to think of the Vales coming out on top. (*Bitterly*) Thank God your grandfather's not around to see the mess this has put us in.

David I'll phone Ainswicke now. (*He gets his mobile phone out*)

Austin (*shaking his head*) It'll have to be later. She's not there at present. Probably in London again, according to Marcia.

David (*helpfully*) I could speak to her.

Austin (*shaking his head again*) Not a good idea. She obviously doesn't *know* about last night's adventure, or she'd have been here with half the County's constabulary, and a home-made gallows. The problem is, we need to speak to Iona before she gets the chance to tell her or anybody else.

Harold (*helpfully*) I've got her mobile number.

Everyone looks at him as he fumbles for his wallet

She gave me her card the first day I met her. (*He finds the card and holds it out*)

David (*moving up to him, taking it relievedly*) I knew you'd be useful one day. (*He reads the card, punches in a number and puts the phone to his ear, moving* cb)

Harold (*after a moment or two*) Any joy?

David She's not picking up. I'll have to try later. (*He closes the phone*)

Brenda (*quietly*) I'm so sorry, Austin.

Austin (*tersely*) Not half as sorry as me. (*Relenting*) But it's no use crying over spilled milk. You were only trying to help. It was just a damn stupid way to do it. We'll have to keep our fingers crossed that she won't want to take it any further.

David (*putting his phone away*) I shouldn't worry. The thought of getting the Monstrance'll be enough to keep her mouth shut. And we'll hear the corks popping from here.

Austin (*dryly*) We hope. (*Rallying*) Well if we can't contact her now, can we get back to what we we're supposed to be doing? I've a dozen or so visitors waiting in the entrance hall, and ——

Father C appears in the doorway L. *He carries a medium-sized and heavy-framed painting, wrapped in an old curtain*

Father C Austin. (*He enters the room*) Mrs Hardwick passed me through. I've been trying to reach you all morning.
Austin (*heavily*) I *am* rather busy, Charles. The Hall's open.
Father C So I noticed. (*He moves down* L *of the sofa*) But I won't keep you. It's just that I felt you should hear the Bishop's decision on the Monstrance as soon as possible. Though a letter will be sent, of course.
Brenda (*rising*) I'll go give Mrs Hardwick a hand.

She smiles wanly at Father C and exits L

Austin (*to Father C*) So?
Father C (*a little embarrassed*) It's always difficult being the bearer of bad news ——
David (*harshly*) We're not getting it back, are we?

Austin gives him an annoyed look

Father C Regretfully not. And unfortunately, I'm entirely to blame for that decision. As you'll recall ... for the past few days I've been delving into the convent's surviving records in the hope of confirming or refuting your claim to the Monstrance. And yesterday afternoon, my efforts were rewarded. I suddenly remembered the Mercer Collection at Farringfield Manor. Now, of course, in the safekeeping of Lady Margaret Stokes, whose family purchased it after the last of the Mercer line died in nineteen fifty-eight.
Austin (*nodding impatiently*) Yes. Yes. I know Maggie.
Father C A quick telephone call confirmed that hundreds of personal letters were part of the collection, and I was invited to examine them without hesitation. It only took an hour or so to find what I was looking for. A letter from Sister Jessamine to her parents, dated seventeen sixty-six, and a diary, written by her younger sister Catherine, later to be Lady Reeves-Mercer, which finally solved the mystery.
Austin And?
Father C (*sighing*) It was quite *sad*, really. Prior to entering the Sisterhood, Jessamine Mercer had been seduced by Sir Martin Reeves' younger brother, Edmund, and sent to Italy to be delivered of his child in secret.

Austin reacts

Following the boy's birth, he'd been entrusted to the church but was later adopted by a Florentine couple ... by the name of Borzoletti.

Harold (*stunned*) You mean Teodoro Borzoletti was Edmund Reeves' son? (*He moves to behind the sofa*)

Father C According to Sister Jessamine. And when, several years after her sister entered the convent, Catherine Mercer married Sir Martin Reeves and honeymooned in Italy, they managed to track him down and tell the Borzolettis the full story.

David (*curiously*) So where did the Monstrance fit in?

Father C It was a gift from Signor Borzoletti to the convent that sheltered the mother of his adopted son.

Harold Then Dr Jones was wrong. The Monstrance isn't a copy.

Father C No. It's the genuine article. But only in the sense that it was made by Gian-Carlo Borzoletti and *not* Teodoro.

Austin But if the Monstrance was a gift from Borzoletti's adoptive father ... what was Sir Martin referring to in his letter? What was *his* gift?

Father C I believe it was this. (*Unwrapping the painting as he speaks*) *The Adoration of the Magi.* The painting that claimed the life of Sister Grace, and almost that of James Reeves-Mercer.

Harold (*a light dawning*) Of course. (*To David*) The reference you found in the diary. He was talking about that. (*Snatching up the diary, skimming through it, then reading*) "But at least the Benefit though somewhat damaged ... required only minor restoration to bring it back to full glory". (*Looking up*) You were right. It didn't make sense. You don't restore damaged goldware ... you repair it. What you restore are buildings and canvasses, et cetera. Why didn't it hit me sooner?

Father C shows the painting to Harold and David. Austin moves slightly upstage so that he can see it too. The audience should only see the back of the frame, which is covered with blackened and age-stained wood

David (*gloomily*) So all this time we've been feuding over a *painting*?

Father C And not a particularly good one, I'm afraid. As you can see, Sister Fidelma's restoration was done with more enthusiasm than skill. Whatever its merits originally, its worth is debatable now. It was only preserved in memory of Sister Grace and that terrible fire. (*He lowers the painting*) If you would like it back, the Bishop is quite happy for me to hand it over, but if not, I can include it with the few remaining items due for auction next month. It may appeal to someone, and the church would benefit.

Austin (*shrugging*) Why not? We've attics full of old junk and we need more like a hole in the head. Do what you like with it.

David (*anxiously*) What about Iona?

Austin (*scornfully*) Can you see *her* wanting *The Adoration of the Magi* on the living room wall? She'd rather have *Madame Defarge Working the Guillotine*, painted in Catholic blood. (*To Father C*) Well thank you for calling, Charles. You've done me a great favour. I may as well kill myself now. (*He turns away*)

Father C looks uncomfortable

David (*moving down* R, *moodily*) I shouldn't worry about it. He's having a bad day. All of us are.

Father C (*realizing*) Ah. Then I'm sorry to add to your troubles. (*Hesitantly*) If there's anything I can do —

David (*sitting on the sofa*) I shouldn't think so, but thanks for the offer.

Father C turns to exit, then hesitates

Father C You're quite sure you don't want the painting? It's part of your history, after all.

David (*shaking his head*) We'd rather have had the Monstrance. Borzoletti or not.

Harold (*curious*) What do you hope to get for it? The painting, I mean?

Father C (*slightly thrown and shrugging*) Twenty or thirty pounds, I suppose. As I said ... whatever value it may have had once, has certainly been reduced by its condition now.

Harold It's still pretty old, though. And the bits that aren't painted over don't look in bad condition. Cleaned up and with the damaged part cut off, it might be worth re-framing. Fragments of old parchment, and stuff go down well with interior decorators. If you really don't want it, I could make you an offer. I know a firm in London who'd do it and wouldn't charge the earth.

David What do you think, Dad?

Austin (*shrugging*) You're welcome to it if you want it. I certainly don't.

Harold (*to Father Carmody*) Will forty pounds be all right? (*He gets his wallet out and extracts some notes*) Or shall we make it fifty?

Father C (*hastily*) No, no. It belongs to Austin. I couldn't possibly.

Harold Then call it a donation to church funds. Please. (*He holds out the notes*)

Father C (*reluctantly taking the money*) Well ... if you insist. (*He hands over the painting*) And now I'd better be off. I really wish I'd been the bearer of happier news.

He smiles at them and exits L

Harold puts the picture on the sofa, its back to the audience, and puts his wallet away

David (*puzzled*) What'd you do that for? You could have had it for nothing.

Harold I know. But ... well I'm not religious, or anything, but I rather like it. Not the over-painted bit of course, but what's left of the original. It looks sort of ... peaceful. (*He picks it up and gazes at it*) Wouldn't mind hanging it in the flat somewhere, if they do a decent job.

David Not in my half of it. I don't want a herd of cows and a couple of Magi goggling at me over breakfast. You can stick it in your own room.

Harold Philistine. It's worth every penny, in my opinion. (*He puts it down again*)

David (*remembering*) And speaking of money, what the hell do we do about Iona? The minute she gets back, they'll be over to Medlock Police Station reporting an assault. (*Puzzled*) I can't believe she's not done it already.

Harold (*hopefully*) It might not come to that.

David (*gloomily*) You don't know them the way we do. Dad's right. It'll be a media bloodbath on Friday.

Brenda enters L, *looking shocked*

Brenda (*faintly*) They've found her body. In the river near Rushton's Mill.

Everyone looks puzzled

Iona Vale's. Jennifer Hardwick's just called her mother.

They look stunned

The couple who found her, *knew* her. They were walking their dog. She must have fallen in last night and been swept away. I'd better call the police.

David What for? It was nothing to do with you.

Brenda (*distressed*) I was the one last to see her alive.

Austin You don't know that.

Brenda (*protesting*) Who else would have been out there in all that rain? (*Wonderingly*) It must have happened after she left me. I told you the grass was slippy.

David (*relieved*) Thank God for small mercies.

Austin (*sharply*) David.

David Sorry, Dad. But don't you see ? It solves everything. If she died before she had a chance to report Treasure's attack on her, we're off the hook. No one knows about it but us. We don't have to bribe her with anything.

Harold He's right. There'll be nothing to connect this place with what's happened.

Austin (*caustically*) Except, perhaps, for the knife. If they find *that* in her pocket, they're bound to start asking questions. Who goes out walking with a kitchen knife tucked away in their coat?

Harold (*to Austin*) I shouldn't worry. It's more likely to be somewhere at the bottom of the river than actually on her. She wouldn't slip it in her pocket with blood on it. All we have to do is keep quiet and it'll just go down as a tragic accident.

David Not very tragic as far as I'm concerned. After what she tried to do, I'd say it was "just desserts".

Austin (*heavily*) Much as I disliked the woman, I wouldn't have wished her dead, but whatever our personal feelings, it's probably best we don't volunteer information. None of us saw her fall, so unless we're questioned directly, we say nothing about last night's events to anyone. Understand?

David and Harold nod

I'll call Marcia later and express our condolences. Now if we could get back to business, we've several visitors waiting.

He crosses to the doors L and exits

David (*to Brenda*) Cheer up, Treasure. No chains and shackles for you, after all. Make yourself some tea, and take it easy whilst Dad and I replenish the family coffers. (*He moves to the door L*) Ask Harry to show you his own family jewel.

He exits

Brenda looks at Harold questioningly

Harold (*hastily*) I think he means my new acquisition. (*He indicates the painting*) It's what's left of the real Reeves-Mercer Benefit. Sir Martin apparently gave this to the convent, and not the famous Monstrance. The family didn't want it, so I bought it from the priest for fifty pounds.

Brenda sits on the sofa and lifts the painting to look at it

A bit battered, but I thought I could have it cut down and re-framed. What do you think?

Brenda brushes at the painting gently

Brenda (*doubtfully*) Celti? Celli?
Harold (*looking over her shoulder*) Sorry?
Brenda The painter's name, I think. You can just see part of it under this awful pink and blue. *Botti*-celli, do you think?
Harold (*taking it from her*) Botticelli? (*Amused*) I wish. (*He peers at it*) But you're right about the letters. It does look like a signature. Cellini, perhaps? Or ... (*Suddenly realizing*) Oh my God. *Ve*-celli. It could be *Ve*-celli. Fourteen seventy-seven to fifteen seventy-six. (*Dazedly*) I don't believe it. Tiziano Vecelli. (*He stares at it in disbelief*)
Brenda Is he famous?
Harold (*incredulously*) Famous? Not only is he famous, he's one of the biggest names in art history. On a par with da Vinci and Michaelangelo. Tiziano Vecelli's the real name of Titian. (*He looks at it in awe*) If it *is* one of his, it's worth millions.
Brenda (*in disbelief*) *That* old thing? But it's covered in cracks and blister.
Harold (*excitedly*) They can clean it up. Remove the over-painting and restore it properly. No matter what it eventually looks like, collectors will give their eye teeth for an unknown Titian. I've got to tell David.

David enters

David Tell me what? (*To Brenda*) Jessie needs more change for the tea room. There's half a dozen in there already, and they're all paying with tens and twenties. Would you mind? I'd do it myself, but there's a coach coming up the drive. Zimmer frames dangling from every window. (*He looks at Harold*)
Harold Forget the coach. Take a look at this. (*He thrusts the painting at him*) It's a Titian.
David (*blankly*) What ?
Harold The famous *painter*, you idiot. Have it cleaned up, and you can name your own price. (*Faintly*) My God. I feel sick. I've just paid fifty pounds for a *Titian*.
David (*warily*) Yes. Well I'm really happy for you.
Harold You don't understand, do you? This little piece of canvas is probably worth more than the Monstrance would have been if

Borzoletti *had* made it. Sell it, and Redston Hall's worries are over. (*He thrusts it at David again*)

David (*moving towards him*) But it's yours. (*He takes it from him looking puzzled*)

Harold No it isn't. I may be here under false pretences, but I'm not a crook. It belongs to your family, and I'm giving it back to you.

David (*frowning*) What do you mean, false pretences? I invited you here.

Harold (*wryly*) But only after I'd dropped enough hints to flatten an elephant. If you hadn't picked up on them, I'd have had to find another reason for coming down to Redston ten days ago.

David (*blankly*) I'm not with you.

Harold (*turning away* R) I was doing someone a favour.

David (*puzzled*) Who?

Harold Dr Jones. (*Turning back*) Look. You'd better sit down. It's a long story and I want to get it off my chest.

Brenda (*to David*) I'll get that change.

David (*frowning*) No, no. Stay here.

Harold (*moving* R) Just over a fortnight ago, she was asked to come down here and evaluate the Borzoletti Monstrance. You can imagine how she felt. The only Borzoletti piece in Britain, hidden from public view for over two hundred years, and *she* was going to handle it. She was so excited, she made a dreadful mistake.

David Oh?

Harold She contacted an old acquaintance from her university days who lived in Redston and told her about it. It was Iona Vale.

David and Brenda react

As you know, there's no love lost between her family and yours, and she spun Dr Jones a story a story about her side of the family being cheated out of Reeves money and begged for her help.

David And she fell for it?

Harold Not exactly. (*Moving down* RF) What Iona *wanted*, was for Dr Jones to declare the Monstrance a fake.

Brenda But why?

Harold To give her the chance to blackmail you into handing it over to them when the Catholics gave it back.

David (*realizing*) So the Monstrance *isn't* a fake.

Harold Unfortunately it is. And that was the problem. As soon as she saw it, she knew it wasn't a real Borzoletti piece and came over here to see if the Reeves-Mercers actually knew about it.

David And where do *you* fit in?

Harold When she told Iona she'd never falsify a valuation, all hell broke loose. Iona threatened to kill her, damage her career, you name it, she'd do it. The Monstrance was theirs by right, and she'd do anything to keep it out of your hands. Jonesie was worried. She remembered an incident at university where one of the students had fallen foul of Iona, and was driven out of Cambridge by a poison pen campaign that eventually ended in suicide. They never found out who sent them, but Iona was certainly a suspect. So she decided to contact me.

David Then you knew her better than you said you did?

Harold Yes. But not that well. We'd spoken a time or two at Steadman and Waterfield, but the main reason she called me was because I was sharing a flat with *you* ... One of the famous Reeves-Mercers, who was right in the middle of Iona's scheme. She asked me to come down to Redston with her, and keep an eye on Iona during the time she was here. You hadn't to know the real reason, of course. I was just to be some sort of protection for her. When I finally *met* Iona, I knew she'd been right. The woman was almost insane. First she tried to bribe and seduce me, and then she resorted to threats. If I didn't help her get the Monstrance, she'd tell my employers I was having an affair with *you*. I couldn't believe it. It was almost surreal.

David You should have *said* something.

Harold How could I? I didn't want to blow my cover. But that's when things went wrong. Your sister stumbled on the truth.

Brenda (*looking up*) Jean?

Harold It was while Dr Jones was here. She mentioned my name. And as we'd not been introduced when she arrived, how could she possibly have known it? And later on, when the Vales referred to her as a woman, when they'd supposedly neither seen or heard of her before, Jeanie jumped to the conclusion that the four of us were working together and went to warn you.

Brenda (*realizing*) So that was what Marcia meant when she told me *I* wasn't Dr Jones' friend? I couldn't understand it at the time.

David But what was Jean doing upstairs? She knew we were all down here.

Harold (*uncomfortably*) Not me. I *had* been in the garden ... and fancied a swim in the pool ... so I went up the back stairs to get my things, and was on the landing when she came rushing out. She looked up and saw me, and went for me like a tiger. "How did she know?" she yelled. "How did she know your name and how did they know Dr Jones was a woman?" Then she slapped me across the face, turned to go, tripped, and fell head-first down the stairs. There was nothing I could do.

Brenda (*aghast*) Oh my God.

David (*stunned*) Then why didn't Iona see you?

Harold She did. She saw everything. But I was in such a panic, I didn't see her. I just raced down the back stairs again, on to the terrace and back into here. I've had nightmares about it ever since. I never laid a finger on her, I swear. It was a total accident.

David (*after a moment*) I'd better call Dad.

Harold Wait. You may as well hear the rest. As soon as Iona heard the Monstrance was a fake, she thought her threats had done the trick and went up to London to celebrate. She wasn't so happy, however, when Dr Jones told her it really *was* a fake and accused her of double-crossing them so she could get the Monstrance for herself. Things got so heated that when Iona threatened her again, she said she'd call the police. Iona backed off at that, but swore she'd get even one way or another, so Dr Jones phoned me after she'd gone and we agreed to meet up and discuss things. She never arrived, though. The next day, I heard she was dead.

Brenda (*horrified*) You think Iona *killed* her?

Harold I've no idea. But she phoned me that night to tell me she'd seen me push Jean down the stairs, and if I wanted her to keep quiet, I'd to come down here and meet her at Ainswicke. It was all rubbish, of course, but I didn't want you believing I *had* killed Jean, so I took the afternoon off and got the two-fifty train. I didn't want anyone to remember me, so instead of getting a taxi, I walked from the station ... just in time for the heavens to open. By the time I got to Ainswicke, I was soaking wet and to round the journey off, the place was totally empty. Not a sign of Iona *or* her mother. I waited in the porch for ages, then gave it up as a bad job and set off back to the station.

David (*coldly*) And that's it? You've told us everything?

Harold Almost. I was just approaching the bridge when I heard shouting. Iona was standing on the edge of the road waving a knife and screaming at something down the bank, so I ran towards her to see if anyone needed help. She must have thought I was going to attack her, because she lashed out with the knife and almost took my head off. What happened next took us both by surprise. The ground she was standing on just collapsed and slid into the river, taking her with it. She was swept away before I'd time to get my coat off.

Brenda (*shocked*) Oh my God.

David And what about Treasure, here? Didn't you think about helping her?

Harold The first time I saw her, she was covered in mud and trying to crawl up the bank. I'd no idea who it was, but I couldn't have anyone knowing I was there when the accident happened, so I took to my heels and got the next train back to London. When I came back today, I didn't know what to expect, but when I heard Iona was dead, I could have cheered. Drowning was the *least* she deserved.

David (*after a moment*) You do know this ends it, don't you? We can't go on sharing the flat. You're partly responsible for Jean's death. If you'd told us what was happening earlier, she'd still be alive.

Harold (*heavily*) I know. And that's one of the reasons I'm giving you the Titian. She loved this place, and I'm grateful for the chance to let the family keep it.

David And you think a piece of old canvas is sufficient payment for her death?

Harold Of course not. Nothing could be. But I think she'd be happy to know Redston Hall wont be turned over to the National Trust.

David (*tightly*) Yes. But she'll never get that chance, will she? (*He turns away*)

Brenda And what about *Mrs* Vale? When she finds out how Iona died, we'll never hear the last of it.

Harold Who's going to tell her? No one else knows. It'll just be another accident.

David Oh, no. I'm not having that. She's not going to wallow in self-righteous grief when if it hadn't been for her and her bloody greed, none of this would have happened. (*He tosses the picture on to the sofa and heads for the door* L)

Brenda Where are you going?

David (*snapping*) Down to Ainswicke to tell the old bitch exactly how her daughter died, and laugh while I'm doing it.

Austin appears in the doorway, looking serious

Austin Can somebody keep an eye on things? I have to go out for a while.

David (*thrown*) What's wrong?

Austin I've just had a call from Tom Wallis at Medlock police station. It's Marcia Vale. When they told her the news about Iona, she collapsed and was rushed to hospital. She died in the ambulance, twenty minutes ago. As next of kin, they want me to identify her.

Brenda (*softly*) Oh my God.

Austin (*flatly*) I shouldn't be that long. (*He turns to go*)

David Dad.

Austin (*turning back*) Yes?

David You'd better sit down. There's something I have to tell you.

Austin looks at him in a puzzled manner then moves back into the room as the Lights begin a slow fade

CURTAIN

FURNITURE AND PROPERTY LIST

ACT I
Scene 1

On stage: Small table. *On it*: remains of breakfast
Two chairs
Lounger
Parasol
Half-empty glass of orange juice
Heavy-looking pelmets and drapes (at french windows)
Long table. *On it*: marble bust, table lamp, bowl of flowers,
    framed photograph of a dog
Pair of wall-mounted lamps (above long table)
Light switches (on wall beside double doors)
Writing desk
Chair
Wall lamps (above writing desk)
Small table. *On it*: bronze statuette, bowl of ceramic flowers
Central white marble fireplace and surround
Wall lamps (either side of fireplace)
Fire-dogs and irons (in hearth)
White fender
Comfortable-looking easy chair
Large matching sofa
Long, narrow table. *On it*: vase of flowers
Long, low coffee table. *On and around it*: discarded sections
    of newspaper
Portraits, scenic views, tapestries and framed photographs (on
    walls)

Off stage: Mug of coffee (**Jean**)
Empty tray (**Brenda**)
Handbag containing small bottle of pills (**Marcia**)
Folded sheet of white paper (**Iona**)

Scene 2

Re-set: Tidy room

Set: Tray, plate of dainty sandwiches, glass of wine (on table)

Off stage: Slim document file (**Austin**)
                 Laden tray of tea and biscuits (**Brenda**)

ACT II
SCENE 2

Strike: Tea things

Re-set: Replace flowers

Set: Glass of whisky (for **Austin**)

Off stage: Glass of water (**Brenda**)
                 Small folded umbrella (**Iona**)
                 Tray holding two mugs of coffee (**Brenda**)
                 Medium-sized, leather bound, ancient-looking diary (**David**)
                 Large kitchen knife (**Brenda**)

Personal: **David**: mobile phone

SCENE 2

Strike: Coffee mugs

Re-set: Tidy room

Off stage: Handbag containing mobile phone and bottle of pills (**Marcia**)
                 Medium-sized, heavy-framed painting wrapped in an
                    old curtain (**Father C**)

Personal: **Harold**: wallet containing banknotes and business card
                 David: mobile phone

LIGHTING PLOT

Practical fittings required: three pairs of wall-mounted lamps, central light,
        table lamp
1 interior, the same throughout

ACT I, SCENE 1

To open: General interior lighting, sunshine on terrace area

Cue 1	**Marcia** exits	(Page 21)
	Lights fade slowly	

ACT I, SCENE 2

To open: General interior lighting, sunshine on terrace

Cue 2	**Father C** hurriedly crosses to doors L	(Page 39)
	Lights fade rapidly	

ACT II, SCENE 1

To open: General interior lighting, heavy-looking sky darkening
        throughout the scene with distant lightning flickering

Cue 3	**Austin**: "Up at the crack of ... dawn."	(Page 55)
	Lightning flickers	
Cue 4	Great crash of thunder	(Page 56)
	Lights fade slowly	

ACT II, SCENE 2

To open: General interior lighting, overcast sky

Cue 5	**Austin** moves back into the room
	Lights fade slowly

EFFECTS PLOT

ACT I

Cue 1 **Jean** screams loudly off stage   (Page 38)
         Series of heavy crashes and shattering of earthenware

ACT II

Cue 2 Throughout ACT II, SCENE 1
         Occasional rumbles of thunder

Cue 3 **Iona**: "... only a few thousands."   (Page 49)
         Rumble of thunder

Cue 4 **David** exits   (Page 56)
         Thunder sounds

Cue 5 **Brenda** exits   (Page 56)
         Great crash of thunder

Lightning Source UK Ltd.
Milton Keynes UK
UKOW030606010513

210018UK00009B/199/P